O Wh

1/3/2022

Losing My Addiction

Owen Jones

Copyright © 3P Publishing
First published in 2022 in the UK

3P Publishing, C E C, London Road
Corby NN17 5EU

A catalogue number for this book is available
from the British Library

ISBN: 978-1-913740-49-8
Cover design: James Mossop

To Helen, Anna and Sophie

Contents

PREFACE

It's all gone

Quite simply, I was on the verge of tears. I had been working on this project, writing about my experiences and thoughts, almost since the day I quit drinking 14 months ago, and it had all gone. Vanished. Forever. I had been rising at 5:00am virtually every day to work on this. It was a labour of love. It was, I now understand, a massive coping mechanism. It was what helped me stay sober, to get better. And now it was gone.

Sixty-five thousand words. Eight chapters. Countless thoughts, ideas, and moments of inspiration captured, now lost forever.

I am of course referring to my first ever book. A book to capture my quit. My thoughts and emotions, as they came and went over that year. As it all happened. Of course, all of this was totally irreplaceable, and the reality of that dawned on me yesterday afternoon. 4:00pm, 19th November 2020. A year lost to lockdown. At least I would have created something out of it. 2020 was going to be my year. My first sober year since childhood. My first book completed, 2020 was looking good for me. Until 4:00pm that afternoon.

As I loaded the recovery disk into my wife's laptop I was full of childlike anticipation. My manuscript had been saved from my broken hard drive. My work was safe. I was but 2,000 words or so from completion. I opened the

Documents folder, and cheerfully navigated to the folder my manuscript was saved in. I was so happy...

But something was wrong.

The folder was...

Empty.

Nothing there.

Like a mad thing I clicked and searched and searched and clicked again and again and again – everywhere on that recovery disk. Everywhere. Absolutely everywhere and in places that weren't even there!

It was lost.

I called the recovery firm. No, that was all that there was, they said. They had spent hours (and I had spent plenty of money) getting everything off my corrupted laptop. There were all my crappy photos, junk files, general stuff that really didn't matter. It was all there, it had all been safely recovered. A 99% success rate on data recovery. A job well done really, from a technical point of view.

But that 1%. Those 65,000 words. A year's work. Gone in an instant, gone when I'd encountered the 'Blue Screen of Death' a couple of weeks before. The bottom fell out of my world. I felt faint, sick, tearful, lost. No anger, no pain. I was empty and shaking. There was literally nothing I could do. I couldn't even cry.

Immediately I knew what had to be done, and I knew it was going to be far from easy. I'd been sober for a year and so I had strength. I also ran bootcamps. I am a marathon runner. I have strength. I have battled through a lot and I'm still here.

It's now 6:43am on 20th November 2020. This is to become the biggest and longest book editing journey ever. I don't have 65,000 words to edit. I have none. I need to dig deep. The edit starts here, and it's a new kind of edit. It's called writing it all over again from scratch.

That's right, all I could do was start all over again. I had to pick myself up, get back in the saddle, put the past where it belongs, and begin at the beginning. Some edit.

My friend Richard wrote to me last night when I told him what had happened. His response:

'If it's worth writing, it's worth writing again.'

I know it's true. I know I have to start again. I also know I must. Add to that the fact that I've done it before, that I have written 65,000 words, then I've had some practice. I am now someone with experience. I have also found that I actually like writing, thank goodness. I know I have other things I was planning on doing. Some will have to wait. I can also approach the process of writing with a more relaxed attitude.

It's odd, but that has just struck me. I was in such a hurry to get this book done that I went at it hammer and tongs; I just attacked it. There was a bit of planning, but I really had no idea. Whether I have one now is a matter for debate, but at least I know what is ahead of me. It's a very long and sometimes treacherous road. I will have times when I'm flying, that I simply don't want to stop. I'll have other days when I'll struggle to get more than three words out!

This time I have 14 months of solid sobriety behind me. This is a book about getting and living sober. It always was (before it was lost). But I do have to ask myself a simple question:

'Isn't it better to write about getting and living sober when I have actually lived *sober, rather than only gone through the process of* getting *sober?'*

First time round, maybe I was on what many refer to as the 'Pink Cloud'. Perhaps I was still in shock at having been able to quit. I was so excited; I was like a kid in a candy shop. Everything was so new and fresh at that time. I'd never experienced anything like it. Yes, I was writing as it unfolded, but maybe I was naïve. Maybe I was too wrapped up in it all, too intensely personal in my writings that reaching out to others would have been too hard. I know some of the stuff I wrote was very raw. Some would have put people off. All that would have been edited out. This time round it won't even go in, not in that form anyway.

Yes, there will be some stuff that is close to my heart and it will come out; it should do. But the good thing, this time round, is that I am writing from a place of solidity, of security, of certainty. Writing about quitting, and trying to help others, as I was still learning, as I was barely out of nappies, as it were, may never have worked anyway. I had no experience, no authority, no right, really. I was a novice; my apprenticeship had not been served. Now, a full year later, I feel in a good place. I feel as if I now have a right to do this, that I'm not some pretender.

I started this section about to cry. 19th November 2020 was a terrible day. So bad that I went to bed earlier than usual to get it out of the way, to consign it to history as soon as possible. I also slept terribly, waking almost hourly through the night. Rising at 5:00am on 20th November, I knew immediately why I'd slept so badly, I knew I had to start again. I knew this book wouldn't appear as if by magic.

I would have to write it. And it would be better than the last one, much better. Lastly, I just wanted to get on with it. Getting started is always the hardest part of anything.

So, up at 5:00am this morning, 30 minutes of exercise, 15 minutes of meditation, and 15 minutes of reading done, I was wide awake and writing by 6:20am. Well before the November sun would rise, I was up and running. Frost on the ground, winter stars twinkling in the sky, this silent time of day is all mine. I guard it well, fiercely even. It is my time to write, and I dedicate myself to do so until this is done. There can be no question. If I can quit drinking overnight, after over 20 years or so of excessive consumption, and love being sober, then there's nothing that can stop me.

I commend myself to this process. This is to be a book about discipline, about making your life 1,000 times better. It needs to be produced with that at the forefront of my mind. You deserve only the best, and Version 2 will deliver that. I owe it to myself, and I owe it to you. Maybe it's for the best that Version 1 will never be seen again. I'll never know.

It will take time to heal, to recover from that loss. It is still intensely painful, and will be for some time to come. I will allow that to work its way out. I will let it do its own thing. I got over the loss of drinking. I'd spent years and years, decades in fact, doing that. I'd simply spent a couple of hundred hours writing. It isn't quite as ingrained in my being. I have my health, my family, my friends, and a great little sideline business, which I love.

After all, only one thing has gone wrong and it is time to put it right, then I'll have another great thing in my life. How long it will take I do not know. It doesn't matter. But it will be done, and I will start right now. A Saturday. At 6:20am. Oh, and this time I'll make a bloody backup!

MY STORY

Blackout!

2018 – September
2:00am

I guess it was around now that I started to come round, and as I did so a wave of panic pulsed through me. Looking round I couldn't understand what was going on, where I was, how I had got there. Instinctively I patted myself down – wallet, phone, keys. All there – all good.

But oh so far from good. Spinning round and round, taking in my surroundings, panic turned to a dread fear. Oh my God, I could be dead – perhaps I should be dead. But I'm not – heaven only knows how that is. Darkness and fields all round me, I knew I had absolutely no idea where I was, that I had emerged from blackout, gradually becoming aware I was conscious and not dreaming, but waking into a nightmare of hellish proportions.

For I was on the A34, walking, stumbling along the middle of a dual carriageway, a major trunk road between Birmingham and Solihull. But I should have been in the bed-and-breakfast I had booked, asleep. Two cars sped by. Which way were they going? Towards my B&B, away from it? Where is my B&B? What's it called? What village is it in? I couldn't answer these questions.

2:30am

I could hardly flag a car down and ask. No longer stumbling but striding with purpose along the side of the road, I had decided that if I walked as if I knew where I was going, I'd get there!

3:00am

Still lost, the fear remained. Conscious, I comforted myself with the fact that I'd simply messed up and that all would be well. I wasn't going to die, I'd get back at some point, just not yet.

A few more cars drove by. I tried to flag them down, desperate for help, but not knowing what I could ask for if anyone stopped. I don't know if anyone did, for I slipped into another blackout there on the A34.

7:00am

My bedroom door, banging. 'Would you like your eggs scrambled or fried?'

I was in bed. Undressed, too. In the B&B. What the hell had happened? I'd been out for a meal with friends in Solihull, and it was a Thursday night. I remembered leaving the office, grabbing a bottle of wine, and drinking it in my B&B before going out. I'd arrived early at the pub we were meeting in and I'd already had a couple of drinks when my friends arrived. I told them I'd just got there and ordered myself a drink, offering to get the first round in. Well, it was their first round anyway. That's where things get a little blurry. There are parts of the meal and evening I recall, others not. I'm sure I was asked to leave a pub at one point, but I don't really know.

What I do know is that this particular evening and following morning wasn't enough to make me stop. I was in the pub at lunchtime the next day, drinking to calm myself down, make the whole thing go away. After all, it was a freaky one-off and I'd learned my lesson.

I'd be more careful in the future. After all, I was a respectable professional man in my 50s, loving family, nice house and car and all that.

Nobody needed to know about this, it would be as if it had never happened, and that would be for the best.

Yes, that would most certainly be for the best.

Where it all started

As a pre-teen, my pewter wine 'glass', reserved for Sunday lunches, was special to me. It was tiny and it made me feel grown up. Nobody else at the table had one and I'd be allowed to have it filled once with red wine. We always had red wine with a roast and this glass first appeared when I was 12 years old. Drinking alcohol didn't cross my mind at the time, it was all about being a big boy, being part of adult society, and I loved it.

But this wasn't where my drinking truly started. That had happened before I had even had a drink. Now I know that sounds crazy, but bear with me on this one. I guess I was about eight years old, I can't quite remember, but I was really still a small child. Well, each year at Christmas my dad used to record a family interview. It was around the time when family cine-cameras were about, the ones that recorded the jumpy, grainy images that you only see now when people go missing and there are TV shows with clips from their childhood; you know the sort. Well, we didn't have one of them, we had a tape recorder!

This particular Christmas, in the early to mid-1970s, I remember quite vividly leaning up against the small step we had between the living room and TV den, and Dad was asking me about my year and what I was looking forward to most about Christmas. He had a little silver stick microphone, you may remember them, and I was almost nervous. You see, even then, I lacked confidence. I was scared of a microphone held by my own father. I was frightened of messing up and it being recorded for ever, for people to laugh at in the future.

Dad asked me if I liked beer! Of course, at that age, I giggled, said I didn't know. Dad asked if I'd like to try some. Goodness knows what was on his mind! Although frightened of the microphone, I was looking at the beer! Dad asked if I thought I would be able to drink it all. I was a small boy, and this was a whole pint of beer. It was a LOT, probably more fluid that I'd ever consumed in one sitting my entire life. At this point memory fails me, but I do know that I didn't drink it all. In fact, I didn't touch it.

That was my first drink.

Although I didn't take it in, physically, I took it in mentally. There was always drink in the house, I knew that. You couldn't miss it with the 1970's house parties going on, and here I was, being invited to join that set of people, to join in with what happened in their world. My brother (being six years older) was already there, of course. He was 14 or 15 at the time. Yes, he'd have wine at dinner, that was just what happened in those days and still does now, I'm sure. And now, there I was, just before Christmas, discussing beer with my dad, as if it were totally normal. Except that I was just eight!

Of course, I simply accepted it. We learn by copying, especially our parents, our greatest influence in those early years. Friendships and outside pressures hadn't really started moulding my views around alcohol at that point. Family was setting my expectations. And those expectations were that it was normal, a part of life. There was no whiff of risk; why should there be?

Dad ended up going to rehab a few years later and in the end his habits did for him. He died too young. By then it was too late for me. I was unstoppable at that point.

11

But for now, back in the 1970s, I'd just been introduced to beer. A year or two later, when the drinks parties began, and I was to be the wine waiter.

1970's drinks parties

Like I said, there was always drink in the house. It was consumed every day. And every now and then that consumption simply skyrocketed. Always a Sunday, always an 11:00am start, and always a smoke-filled living room.

This was my education, how I truly learned all about alcohol, and how I really started to see it. These were the infamous 1970's drinks parties, that suburban staple of middle-class excess, coupled with an explosion of brown, orange and corduroy flares. Such style! The 11:00am gin and tonic. Whisky so soon after breakfast. Wine by the bucketload. And as a pre-teen, what the heck was I doing there? Being the dutiful son, of course. And I loved it.

I had a job to do, and it was drilled into me just how important that job was. I was to move amongst the guests, ensuring glasses were always filled, and nibbles occasionally distributed. There were smoked oysters, cheese and pineapple sticks, crisps and peanuts. Mum didn't do vol-au-vents in those days – they'd come later!

And then there was the booze. 1.5 litre bottles of the stuff, no point holding back. Never great quality, this was diesel for the masses. Decanted into used Paul Masson carafes for serving, around I moved, pouring, pouring, pouring wine. There was a buzz about it all, these parties were noisy, fun and at times very, very silly. Lunchtime drinking turned these adults, I found back then, into laughing, joking, loud and fun people.

A critical piece of evidence in favour of drinking was being lodged into my mind. It was fun and brought people together. Not only that, but the most important people in my life were encouraging me to be part of that scene. Maybe

I never had a hope. Maybe I was, from that point on, destined to become a problem drinker. I don't think I'll ever know for sure, but this environment certainly didn't make me turn away in horror. You see, I never got to see the unpleasant side of it all. It wasn't on show, and if it's not on show it doesn't exist.

Late developer

One of the phrases that sticks with me most in life, and started making its way into my consciousness during this period, this was one by which my parents referred to me, to my face, and to their friends. They would openly state that I was a 'late developer'.

Thanks!

But what did this mean, and might it have had any influence on my becoming a problem drinker?

The thing is, I understand precisely what this reference did to me. I knew it at the time and I never challenged it. I believed it to be true, absolutely true, and trusted it completely. And this is exactly where the problem started. You see, for me, at the time, to be told I was a 'late developer' was never a problem. I was the younger of two brothers, and as I see it, my elder brother was and still is far brainier and more successful (in many ways) than I have ever been.

This was, whilst young, great, because my 'late developer' status meant that I could believe that I would, in time, develop into a success. Because of this, there was little point putting any effort into learning and growing. After all, it would all work out in the end. I would develop at some point, so I needn't worry. Having been given this label, I took full advantage of it. I was lazy. I didn't appreciate that I actually had to put the effort in, that the reason my brother was ahead of me was actually down to hard work. There was of course an element of natural ability, but that wasn't the real difference, as I now understand, some four decades later.

Back in my young and formative years, all this 'late developer' stuff gave me great freedom, as you can imagine. I was never burdened with too much work, as it was ingrained in me that all would come good in the end. Deep down, and built up over many years, I can now look back and can see that I really believed it would simply happen, that I would magically develop. Of course, I never did. And over time this gnawed at me. I never seemed to progress. I never seemed to get on.

To emphasise this point, on leaving university my tutor took me to one side and suggested that, once in the real world of work, I might like to consider working quite hard. So by the time I should have developed, I was already running behind.

As time went by and from an early age when I really should have been laying the foundations of life, I was in the pub. In my gap year, I spent most of my evenings, and earnings, on drinking beer. *Well, why not?* I thought. I was enjoying myself. All I was actually doing was creating a lifetime of drinking, of not progressing. And over time, as drinking became an addiction, I started playing no active part in my own development. I simply entered a downward spiral. I now believe that by the age of 18 I was addicted. I'd already become an alcoholic. I just didn't know at the time.

The more I drank, the less chance I had of developing. I didn't have the time or energy to do it. I didn't have the inclination to either, I was a 'late developer'. This was the label I had been given just as I emerged into being a boy, and I guess it should have been shed by the time I hit my late teens.

I still wore it long into my late 40s and early 50s.

I truly believe that it was only when I quit drinking that I finally shrugged it off, that I started growing, maturing, becoming a man. Until then, drinking, I was but a boy, and an unhappy one at that. How many times have you heard the following?

It was only when I stopped drinking that I started growing up.

How true is that? I'm just so glad that I have now started to grow up. It's about time really. When young, even though I was a late developer, I wanted to be up with the best of them, and made myself out to be more than I was. I would use my imagination, as it were, and tell what would become known to me as tall stories.

Tall stories

Part of my formative years were made up of my frantic attempts to make friends, but I was not good at this. It would have been around the time I was seven or eight years old, and we had just moved back to the UK from a few years in the USA, where Dad had been posted for work. I was friendless, didn't know anyone here in the UK, and felt extremely insecure in myself.

But I knew I had something nobody else did, a life in a foreign country (this was in the early 1970s, just as worldwide travel was starting to open up), so I made up stories, trying to make myself interesting, trying to impress. I even started to believe the stories myself. I was making up a life I'd never had and making it out to be real, embroidering the truth, and eventually I was called out by my teachers, to my parents, for telling tall stories. Lies, basically.

This hurt me, even though I was in the wrong. I guess I could tell I was different from everyone else, who seemed to get along without great effort. I was always trying to make myself out to be more than I was, and I always came unstuck. This carried on through senior school and into university.

Even so, I continued, and it hurt. I wasn't learning, and I soon found that a few beers would easily make it go away. And in many ways it did, to start off with. I found some great drinking friends at university. I was a decent hockey player, got into the Second XI, and discovered that it was a great drinking team. I had found my home at last. I drank that year, and I enjoyed it like no other. I could simply be me, a drunken oaf without a care in the world. The problem is that I was simply strengthening the path I was to follow, inevitably, for a great many years to come. Slowly, inexorably, I was becoming more and more of a problem drinker, an alcoholic.

Well before then, and once done with wine-waiting for my parents, I was spirited away to boarding school. It was 1979, and the next stage of my life was beginning.

Schooldays

Thirteen years old, fresh faced and somewhat scared, I've always lied about my time at school. I didn't enjoy it from the first letter I sent home, describing the place like a prison, to when it was over. Five years of my life that wasn't at all to my liking. It's no wonder I have virtually no remaining friends from what many consider to be the most important time of our lives. That's right, maybe not even one. It's very personal, but not altogether surprising. I am, not so deep down, simply a frightened, shy individual, and found that environment really hard. I was amongst highly confident, accomplished people, and I felt way, way behind them. In truth, saying I enjoyed my schooldays is probably about as far from the truth as you could get, but that's how it was for me.

Alcohol helped. It provided me with an identity. Along with hanging out, on the periphery, with the smoking lot, drinking gave me something I could feel comfortable in. It was as if I sought the easier way. Rather than trying to better myself and work my way up the food chain, I had decided, as I see now, to become a bottom-feeder. I'd sneak to the pub on a Sunday afternoon, a Tuesday evening, Wednesday between lessons if I could, once in the Sixth Form. I'd go on bike rides, buy Cinzano, and drink it in the woods. I'd also have vodka hidden in bean bags in my tiny study. I was one of the school's drinkers, and I smoked a lot then, too.

But never in the holidays. It would be too awful if Dad caught me. I didn't care about being caught at school, as I wouldn't have Dad's ire to face, just an awkward phone call home. I could handle that!

It seemed that throughout life, and more so during my schooldays, I have been surrounded by self-assured people, those that could easily make lifelong friends and alliances, had strong social networks, and even now stick with them and seem to thrive. Looking back, I never once found myself as part of this scene. I was always too scared to put myself forward for fear of looking stupid, or saying the wrong thing. When I did manage it, I generally felt something of an intruder, a 'Cling-on', as it were.

I found myself being almost perpetually silent, either too scared to contribute or believing that what I had to say would make me look stupid. In such groups I was a lost soul. Individually, I got on fine with people. In a group, I was a terrified mouse.

I knew what I should be doing to get on in life, where the routes to success lay. However, I didn't have the guts to follow them, preferring to wait for the next one, by which time I believed I would have plucked up the courage to get on. As each passed, the worse it got. Inevitably, I never got on.

Very early on then, I was emotionally adrift, needing to cling on to something. I wasn't, or so I told myself, suited to certain social groups, so ignored them completely. Others were so far removed from my experience in life that there was no way I could head in those directions. So I found myself hanging out with people I now realise I shouldn't have done. I did things I should never have done, that would never do me any favours, and that simply ended up making me feel more and more distanced. But at least I had something to hang on to, however fragile. It was easy, too. I felt that I didn't really need to make an effort, just 'being'

21

was enough. It was a tough time, and it was a time that was shaping me more and more every day.

One year, and I still can't work this one out a lifetime later, we ended up trying to make homebrew at school. We left it over the Easter holidays to do its stuff. Caught doing this, I guess, was an inconvenience, but it also felt quite cool. It was so very audacious. It may have failed, but who cared? It was a great effort! Over time, it's ended up as just another story in my drinking journey, one that continued well into my '50s.

But once out of school, it was time to take a gap year, and discover myself. It was time to find my identity.

Falling in with the wrong crowd

Who I hung around with, the role models I related to and those I emulated had a profound effect on my development and, naturally, my drinking. It is no different for anyone else.

As a result, I would fall in with the wrong crowd. It was partly deliberate, as I had to be part of something. And it was partly out of desperation; nobody else would have me. My social skills were poor. I was excruciatingly shy and silent and I was surrounded by loud, confident, people who were finding and making new friends with ease. I couldn't make a single one, and as it made me down in the dumps, this would show in my demeanour and make it even harder.

This sounds like a 'poor me' sob story, but it is exactly how it was. Life was not fun; it wasn't a pleasure. Every day was hard and drinking came easy. I'd already spent half my gap year sitting on a bar stool in the village local, drinking all my earnings. That was a life I slotted into, where I could vanish into a beer and feel better. So, I spent a lot of time alone. There really was no 'wrong crowd'; I never found the right one. Correction, I found the right one, and then ran away from it. I knew it was the direction I should be heading, but after years of waiting for the right time, the right group to come along, I succumbed to the same inertia.

I was able to watch my peers go off and do what I wanted to do. I could easily have done the same; I had the talent and knowledge to do so, but just had no ability to take that first step. Every time something came along it was as if I'd say, 'Oh, after you', politely step aside and let someone else go on ahead of me. The right crowds therefore passed me by, and I was left with what remained. Maybe I didn't fall in with the wrong crowd, maybe I simply allowed myself to settle with whatever and whoever was around at the time.

So where did I end up? Who did I end up with? I tended to stick with those who would have a beer or two more than anyone else after the game. I'd make sure I hooked up with the person who was going to be first to go out in the evening; I needed to start earlier than everyone else. It's therefore questionable whether I ended up with a crowd at all.

I certainly didn't have a circle of friends, if that's what we mean. As I have passed through each stage of my life, I have had a close friend or two at any one time, then moved on. As I have moved on, I have either not bothered to keep in touch with them, or those friends have not done so with me. Either way, the connection I had with them could never have been all that strong. I have no remaining friends from school, three from university. Even now, although I have been in my current job for five years, I have not one single friend at work.

However, none of us is really alone in this world. Group identity is such an important part of being and we all fit in somewhere. Finding where that is can be a challenge, but with effort we can all get there.

Group identity

In a sense, we are all part of one community or another. We are part of the human race. We may be male or female, we may be parents, we are all children, and so we can go on breaking down and down into smaller and smaller groupings. We are all a part of numerous groupings, whether we know it or not.

As we grow, we tend to fall in with certain groups. Some we choose and some we are made to be part of, and all these help to shape us as individuals. For someone like me, this groups thing was a double-edged sword, and to cope with it I often turned to what I knew, from experience, helped: alcohol.

Being a drinker, I found a community. I didn't have to be with other people to be in it. I didn't have to be drinking to be in it. But I knew that, wherever I was, I was part of something. I was a drinker. Looking back, I see how it led me deeper and deeper down the rabbit hole. You see, being a drinker led me to other drinkers, to other drinks and to different situations. Sitting alone in a bar, on a night away on business of some sort, I would say hello to folk as they passed.

Those who did not drink would never stop. But you could bet your bottom dollar that, each and every night, I'd catch a drinker, and bingo, I'd have someone to talk to, maybe for a few short minutes but invariably longer. Alcohol in, hotel loneliness over.

I could have been part of any other group. Some people would run, or swim, or read, or walk or watch a film. There were other unseen groups. Some were right there, in my face and wholly available to me. For instance, I'd turn down invites from colleagues to go to the cinema, or grab a takeaway rather than eat the hotel's dull buffet. The problem was that I knew I would want to drink the way I drank and they wouldn't. I also knew I couldn't face an evening out if it was going to be like that.

So I'd let them head off, maybe order a beer, and strike up a conversation with a total stranger, generally one that was as dissatisfied with being alone in a hotel as I was. I'd found a member of my group. They were easy to spot, spend a few minutes with and then separate from. I don't recall seeing any of them ever again and so it didn't matter if we met when I was on pint one or pint five.

We were merely individuals who shared some kind of group identity, were peers for a while as we propped up the bar and then went our separate ways. Looking back, considering this, it's a kind of sad identity, isn't it? But as a dependent drinker, a quiet night in one bar with drinks on tap has got to be better than a dry cinema with sober work colleagues. At the time it was, or so I thought.

But what happens when that new friend drinks until 5:00am? I can't survive on less than two hours of drunken sleep before a breakfast meeting. But one day, in Berlin, I'd had to. My employer had flown me out to Germany for a two-day workshop, and I somehow found a late-night drinking buddy. I got through the next day, but it was close run thing.

Or what happens when the friend doesn't exist and instead becomes 'just one more drink' in the hope of his arrival, ending up as a day off work the next day due to 'migraine'?

A night with a virtual group, by which I mean drinking alone whilst pretending to wait for an imaginary friend, can go as badly wrong as with a real one. In the mind, one is as real as the other and, when it comes to drinking, just as dangerous.

On gaining sobriety, bar-prowling became a thing of the past. Always a runner, even when I was drinking, I now run, shower, eat and read when away in a hotel for work. It's an awful lot more relaxing, choosing the right group to join, and fitting in with its identity, than it is to drink.

But where did this all come from? How do we become the person we are? How was it that I'd turned into a bar stool, too frightened to step out into the world on my own? How much of this might have had its roots in my upbringing? Perhaps it was because I was a little late getting going, and perhaps it was because the years of transitioning from child to adult – my university years – can be summarised in one word:

'Opt'

This will resonate with six or seven people, that's all. It is something that I was unable to resist. Not once in my time at university did I decline the 'opt'. This was the 1980s, a time before university fees became burdensome loans. Higher education was free. There were fewer universities and students. As a result, I believe university life was less pressured and students were not quite so serious about study as they seem today. It may be me, but when going back to visit my university a year or so ago, half the bars had been converted into study zones and coffee shops. It sucked. That says it all!

So, back to the 'opt'. In simple terms, when faced with the choice of an evening of study or drink, the 'opt' would be to take the 'opt'ion to have a drink. Anyone in the group could call for an 'opt' at any time. There was no compulsion at all. Those who wanted to study or do anything else were under no obligation to abandon that and 'opt' for drink. I really don't recall where the concept came from, or who named it, but it was so very powerful.

Needless to say, as soon as an 'opt' was called, I'd drop everything and take up the suggestion. If no call came, I'd get impatient waiting for it. In the end, if the waiting became too much, the call would inevitably come from me. There were a few nights when there was no call at all; we did do some work, you see. But most nights, the call would come, and I would drink. And if no call came, I would call it for myself. If that meant drinking alone, then I would do just that, sitting in the corner of the bar with a beer and a book, or just chatting to whoever happened to be there.

This was the beginning of my daily drinking habit and in those days, I'd regularly down eight pints a night. Mornings were never an issue. Three years of Geography didn't include lectures before 11:00am!

It was when I hit the world of work that matters changed. A bit.

Through the 1970s drinks parties and my special wine glass, to Cinzano and home brew at school (where we also had a bar for over-17s), and on to the infamous 'opt' at university, let's just say my formative years all had one thing in common: alcohol.

I can't think of any single reason why I started drinking. Maybe it was because it was always there in front of me, always being consumed. Maybe it was because I was painfully unsure of myself. Maybe it was because I wanted to have an identity. Maybe it was because I came to like the feeling of being drunk. Or maybe all of this mixed up and shaken around, a right messy cocktail!

Whatever happened, I ended up a problem drinker. I knew this very early on. It was obvious when I was at school. I knew it, maybe other people could see it. Nobody ever said anything – but you can't really, can you?

So I'd managed to get through school and uni, and ended up with a job on a management training scheme with some vaguely unknown company in Ellesmere Port. I would also work in Warrington and Manchester at this time, and was living in and around Chester. It should have been now that I would take off into a glittering career.

But again, alcohol called to me and stopped me in my tracks.

Whilst in Chester, I lodged with a wonderful couple. They were heavy drinkers, and had friends who were the same. I didn't know this until I started lodging with them, although I soon slotted in very well with their lifestyle, being of a similar persuasion where alcohol was concerned. Anyway, they had a friend called Merv who was a big, blond, affable, avuncular character, full of great stories and a seemingly endless capacity to drink. I was an impressionable young man just starting in the world and keen to fit in. He was also the first and only person I've met who was at Woodstock, so he was even more special to me for that. I never did let on though, that would have been weird. I felt almost as if Merv took me under his wing and I liked that. He would speak, from time to time, of what he called a "Hobecker". At the time there was a fashionable continental lager called Hobeck, and a "Hobecker" would simply be a bender, drinking Hobeck. This brand had become a verb, had taken on a new life and meaning. It was now an event as well, and it had meaning. Merv had become the advertising agent's dream, a promoter in himself.

Although I never went on a true Hobecker, that word has stayed with me throughout my life. The strength of the image and its vivid clarity has meant that it is lodged in my mind. Until recently, I would still peer over bars looking to see if they stocked Hobeck. I never did see it again.

The point here is that a strong friendship with a strong association with a particular event, product or whatever is something we will carry around with us for a very long time, if not forever. If that association is alcohol, we will be constantly reminded of it as we go through life. There will be triggers everywhere.

But it doesn't have to be a specific friendship, other groups and alliances also form. In the UK, one such group is the Campaign for Real Ale (CAMRA). Their purpose is really very clear, and they have been extremely successful in promoting traditional ales across the UK. Smaller, specialist breweries have been founded and discovered considerable success as a result of the actions of this group. No individual brands are advertised or promoted, just the type of product – ale. Festivals abound. The fans are passionate. The members are every bit as dedicated as ardent football supporters. And even away from the environment in which they practise their passion, everyone will be aware of what it is.

The reason I mention this is that it is not only – in fact, it's only partly – the big-spending companies that are able to permeate our lives and have us absorb alcohol into them. Individual friends influenced me day by day and over a lifetime. Clubs, festivals and interest groups also abound and entered my psyche. I may have been able to see and filter much of the highly visual and audible advertising on the TV, radio, social media, billboards on the sides of buildings and so on, but it's hard to shut out a lifestyle that much of society lives by and is, in essence, normal daily life.

Once we are able to see this, that perhaps the best advertisers and promoters of drinking alcohol are the invisible ones, the silent ones, those who don't even realise they are doing it, we can bring ourselves to a heightened sense of awareness. We can see how much our lives are dominated by direct and indirect references to alcohol. Once our eyes have been opened to the Hobeckers out there, we are able to make conscious decisions about how we live our lives. Our friends can only lead us down the garden path if we are willing to go, or if we are unaware of what's at the end of it. Once we know, we can make decisions, and wrestle back control over our lives.

Remaining in ignorance is no place to be. Once I was able to see and understand what was in front of me, then I was more than halfway there. Over the next few days and weeks, have a think about just how much drink-related information comes your way other than through specific and clear advertising. I think you'll be surprised, maybe horrified. You'll wonder how you missed it, but also realise how easy it is to get caught up in it. With this knowledge, you'll be able to start unravelling the tangle you have got into, see what's out there and make better choices.

That can only make quitting easier. And an easy quit is what we all want, isn't it?

But first, we need to do the groundwork and, as The Greatest, Muhammad Ali, famously said:

'It is better to suffer in the training than to fail in the battle.'

Before then though, I'd like to take us back to my story, and find out a little bit more about how I began to come off the rails. One of the key facts was that I would often end up...

Living a lie

Not so long ago I was having a very rare peek at Twitter. It's a platform I really don't use. I guess I'm old school and stick to Facebook. No Instagram, no Snapchat, I have no interest in them. I honestly don't know what they are about, but what I saw on Twitter was a quote that went along the lines of:

'I don't get into trouble every time I drink, but when I do get into trouble I've been drinking.'

This made me reflect on my own past, and what had gone wrong with it, or where I had acted in ways contrary to the norm. What I won't take you on is a journey through all my drinking days. There were days I wish had never happened, things I wish I'd never said, things I wish I'd never done, and all those things that would NOT have happened if I had been sober and in control. You see, we all have our own stories, our own crisp or hazy memories of these, and we can all conjure them up in our heads. Not all of them need to come out!

Now and then, when my wife was away visiting her parents, I'd go on a short bender. I'd be 'sick' from work, and go and live in the pub for a few days. I'd put my work shirts into the washing basket, barely worn but enough to pretend, to hide my deception. I'd throw food away in an attempt to prove I'd eaten it. What a shameful way to behave, devious, dishonest and unfair on everyone. Since quitting, I have had zero days off work, and looking back over the years I can honestly say that the only reason I did was because I was hungover (or, officially, had a migraine).

How that added to the stress though! Living a dishonest life is not easy, but having a drink to push that discomfort away worked every time, as it brought blessed relief. The thing was, because I was either drinking or thinking about drinking pretty much all the time, I was never able to escape fully. Even now, I am clearly thinking about drinking a lot, as I work my way through creating this book but, as I'm now a non-drinker, it's like water off a duck's back. I am no longer bothered by it.

Living a life of deception and lies is tiring; it grinds you down. It certainly ground me down, and so often I would look up, trying but failing to see a light at the end of the tunnel. It wasn't until I started to educate myself, to learn about alcohol's ways, the science, the myths and the escape routes, that I knew which way to look. Even so, I managed to keep on drinking through it all. How is that? It's actually a feature that us drinkers share with one another, and that came in very useful when I finally quit:

As drinkers, we have stamina!

As drinkers, we have to keep our stories straight, consistent, in case we are found out. I needed to keep my wits about me and it's hard work. In a weird sense, I had to put in quite a level of effort to allow myself to keep drinking. There is a massive façade I needed to maintain, over many months and years, to keep on boozing. Hour after hour of finding reasons or excuses to drink, planning days out so I could ensure there would be some good drinking time in there, planning who'd be driving to which events; all this took real dedication to the cause. Living a life like this, it's clear I had a problem with alcohol, but it also shows us, if we look hard enough or in the right direction, that we have a way out.

Heavy, dependent and alcoholic drinkers all have a focus and determination that ensures they get their booze whenever they need it. We have a strength in this, as well as in keeping up a façade of some sort all the time. Us drinkers are constantly hiding, from the truth, from ourselves, and from other people, and this also takes effort. We have very high levels of stamina, keeping up appearances for years at a time. It is this stamina, this strength, that we can use to our advantage.

As drinkers, we are determined, dedicated, resilient and resourceful people. These are all hugely positive character traits, and yet I used them to make sure I always got a drink, or to concoct a catalogue of lies and deceptions behind which I lived my life. Perhaps, in time, it was these very characteristics that enabled me to quit successfully. We'll look into that later on.

But for now, quitting wasn't going to happen for quite some time, and until then, the welcome that would greet me as I entered a pub would be along the lines of:

'The usual, sir?'

Now that my own daughters are working in pubs, they tell me that as soon as they see a customer walking through the door they'll start pulling a pint, knowing exactly what they want.

Talk about predictable! As punters we'll even put on a mock 'Let me think, oh OK, the usual then' routine. This makes us feel like we have a choice in the matter, and that we are in control of our drinking. The very act of considering, whilst already knowing the answer, is a massive giveaway. We are trying to prove to ourselves and to others that we are just going about our daily business and making choices along the way. But we are not.

And what was the usual, for me? Greene King IPA in the pub, Blossom Hill crisp white wine at home.

Neither of them are exactly standout drinks. Each is mass-produced and inoffensive. They tasted absolutely the same every time I drank them, and I drank them daily. Everything about them was totally predictable, and I knew the price of each in different pubs and off-licences or supermarkets. If that's not sticking to the usual, then I don't know what is. I guess I was a loyal customer.

The advertising, directly or indirectly, had worked its magic. I was now a dedicated, fully paid-up member of each of the brand's offerings, IPA and white wine. And each time I ordered or poured 'the usual' I was personally reinforcing this message. I was now doing the advertisers' job for them, to myself.

As a little aside, it's interesting to note that when quitting, we are often confronted by the challenge that soft drinks are limited in range and flavour. I'd say sticking to one wine and one beer is far more limiting. And experimenting with different soft drinks and flavours is a lot cheaper and less risky (sodas don't generally go off in the bottle either – many wines do! Well, if they are given the chance.)

This loyalty actually made life so much easier; I never had to think about what to buy. The stress of making a choice was removed, and it also meant I could get to drinking it more quickly. I could even imagine it before I had swallowed a drop, I was drinking 'virtually', thus satisfying some of my needs (calming nerves, relieving shakes) even sooner. Often, I'd have the exact money ready to pay for the drink when I went to the pub. There would be no waiting for change and so I could pick up the beer right away and it made me feel good to make the barman's job easier!

If I wanted a few drinks, I'd even count out my cash at home and work out exactly how many I could afford before heading out. Knowing exactly what I was going to drink, and its price, has its advantages.

Once at this point, however, carefully counting out the coins, searching for the odd penny hidden behind the sofa, I was at one of my lowest ebbs. It was also a time when I would take the odd day off work sick. The sickness would be self-induced, and always came about when my wife was away.

So, I was loyal to Blossom Hill and Greene King. If Greene King wasn't available, I'd have the nearest equivalent. All would be well until I'd reach a tipping point, a certain number of drinks in. At this point, a dangerous level of drunkenness, all bets would be off and any semblance of control would be gone. It's at this point that 'the usual' drink vanishes as a concept, and is replaced by 'the usual' drunken irrational behaviour. It's predictable.

Let's consider two examples from my back catalogue of drinking experiences.

First, taken from my last ever drinking session, a two-day event starting on a Saturday with friends and ending on Sunday, alone and making the decision never to drink again.

There was nothing inherently special about the day. Every autumn, a group of us would go out on a pub crawl. We'd visit a few pubs in the afternoon, head back to Steve's house for a curry and a daft film in the evening, and all head off the next morning. This last time was somehow different, and it was around pub five that it all started to go wrong. I'd been drinking 'the usual' all day and I guess my mind got into what I thought was its mischievous mood, so I bought a round of shots of some description. I seem to recall sambuca, or Jägermeister, neither a wise move for a mid-afternoon sup!

Looking back, I realise I did this for two reasons. First, I had lost control of my drinking and had gone off the rails. Second, I was seeking approval from the others. The approval I was after was that it would be OK for *me* to drink these shots. After all, everyone else would have to, so I'd not be on my own. But there was a deeper approval I was after, too, and one that's at the heart of my drinking. I was after social approval. I was being a generous friend, thinking of others. I would therefore be less alone, less of an outsider. I've always felt that way and drinking helped ease that pain. Getting this round of shots in for everyone made me feel better. I was a giver.

But was I? I was seeking their friendship, their acceptance and approval of me. That makes me sound more like a taker – and it's probably not too far wrong where alcohol was concerned. I didn't understand or see that at the time. I do now, and see it as a desperate act of a frightened individual. As long as I believed that alcohol would remove my fear and make me feel less desperate, I would remain this way.

The thing is, as soon as I removed alcohol from my life, that fear and desperation started to lift. Alcohol had never helped it after all.

Looking back on getting these drinks in, I was hardly loyal, hardly consistent, hardly predictable and steady. I couldn't even stay true to the drink that I considered as 'the usual'.

The second example is closer to home. It involved nobody but me and it goes like this. I'd been drinking all evening, having bought a couple of bottles of wine on the way home, just in case. I never had a stock of wine or beer in the house, I was drinking hand to mouth, as it were. At around 11:00pm, I realised that all the Blossom Hill had gone, that somehow I'd managed to get through two bottles without realising it. The issue now was that it wasn't time for bed, not for a drunk, anyway! Therefore, I needed to find a drink, any drink, just one more, a nightcap as it were.

We don't have a drinks cabinet, but keep a few bottles of gin, some port and a bottle of Malibu on the floor next to the piano. I wouldn't go near the gin, it wasn't mine anyway, I really can't stand Malibu and love port, so port it would have to be. One of the great things about port is that the dark bottle it comes in hides how much has been drunk, or remains, so sneaking a small glass generally goes unnoticed. Further, the bottle was boxed, so the theft would be invisible.

And what do these two little stories tell us?

I was a loyal drinker, sticking to 'the usual' until a point was reached when, quite simply, anything would do.

Understanding that this tipping point existed, and that I only drank because I was drunk, was a great help in illuminating just where my drinking had got to. I had to get it out of my life.

Recognising this, I could use it as tool to help me hold it all together in sobriety.

These two pillars of understanding and recognition, as borne out by my drinking behaviour, were key to making my quit successful and provided me with great strength.

Maybe you have similar stories or experiences you can draw on to strengthen your resolve and solidify your quit. I'm sure there's something out there; we all have our little habits.

The issue was that my habit had started to impinge on my ability to do my job, so I was forced to take action. I needed to see someone about my drinking. Work had noticed a problem and I had no choice. I went because I had to, and I understood it was for my own good, but my heart wasn't in it at the time.

So off I went to see a therapist. Whilst there, for the ten sessions I had, as paid for by my employer's healthcare package, I was encouraged to look back over my past, hunting for events, episodes and so on that had had a profound effect on me and influenced the way I behaved.

I know a few things that might have made me upset when I was younger. People say stuff; it happens to us all. Maybe that affected me, maybe not. It's in the past, so I can't do anything about it. And yet one of the biggest pieces of advice we are given in confronting our drinking, in trying to quit, is to dig up the past. It was certainly the case for me, in the 2000s.

Costing me nothing other than my time and commitment, each Tuesday evening I would head off for an hour on the couch, dredging up memories and analysing why I drank on them. But before I go on, let me allow you into a secret. The only thing I can actually remember about those sessions was that on the way there, the country road I drove along had a sharpish right-hand bend on it, with a solid stone wall facing it. It was perfect, I thought, for a direct hit. Drive at 100-plus mph, miss the corner – head on – instant end in a crumpled mash against a massive stone wall. That's what I remember about those sessions. Now I don't think my head was in the right place those days, and I never did take the idea of ending it against that wall any further.

Even sober, in therapy, my mind was all over the place. That was what needed sorting out before even considering the drink, but I was there about my drinking, so that's what we talked about.

There we were, busy digging up the past and trying to work out why I drank. Here it was that I lied again, or maybe embellished the truth and also hid it. I made out that my childhood was far more traumatic than it really was. I hammed it up. As for my actual drinking, she only got half the story, heard about half the amount I really drank. She was never going to know, so why should I tell her? I also reckoned she'd never been drunk in all her life and guessed that she was teetotal.

Teetotal and therefore clueless about drinking. I had a free pass. But what about the whole point in seeing her – to stop or cut down my drinking? Well, cut down, of course. I didn't want to stop. I didn't know there is a binary choice for alcoholics. *Drink or Don't Drink.* There is no halfway house. Either she didn't know that or, if she did, she kept it to herself. Whatever the position, it wasn't helping me, and with me pulling the wool over her eyes, she wasn't able to help me. Maybe she saw through me. If she did then surely her professional duty was to call me out? I don't know, but I kept going for the full ten weeks of the programme.

During those ten weeks, each session was spent looking deeper and deeper into my past, peeling layer after layer off the proverbial onion, seeking the truth, that little nugget that, once exposed would lead to – what? Some a-ha moment where I suddenly understood why I drank, how to stop, or what? I don't know! If we had found that miraculous event, episode or whatever, I have no idea what we would have done about it. Yet that was what we were seeking, I'm sure, and answers or just *the* answer.

But what we found were not answers. With each layer we peeled off that onion, we found more pain, more unpleasant past experiences. I recall I was asked to dig deeper into them, to find out the matter at the heart of each of these. I spent ten weeks dragging up painful memories, reliving past unpleasantness and bringing it into the present.

One of the reasons I drank was to take the pain away, and here I was making life more painful. This therapy was fuelling my drinking, not helping me cut down or stop. Maybe I didn't drink as much as normal in that period, but perhaps that was more to do with the fact that I was very conscious that I was on a programme. Had I not been on it, spending so much time in the painful past would have been unbearable, but for numbing it with drink.

What did I learn from this brief period of my life, taking action on the advice I was given that I should see a therapist, a specialist? I think there were, for me, these lessons.

First, living in the past is not where I needed to be. It had happened and I needed to leave it there. I needed to see a bright future of love, happiness and fun to help me quit drinking. I did not need to see scenes of darkness, sadness and depression. Those don't inspire me, nor do they fill my heart with hope. The past is just that, and I can't change it; it exists only in my mind, and it's best left well alone.

Second, and despite peeling back the layers week by week, we would never have found what we were looking for. The answer to my not drinking in the future can't be found in my past, my drinking past. I now understand that the answer to my not drinking is only ever to be found in the now and in the future. That was where I needed to look, and that's where I found it. And just to be clear, this is how it worked for me, how I made sense of it. I am not able to be you and know what might work for you; I'm just here tell you how it was and is for me. What you do with my words is entirely your choice.

Finally, I started those therapy sessions wanting to control my drinking. I wanted to continue, but stop getting so drunk so often. I simply wanted to drink like a 'normal' person. Now I know I can't, that there is no cutting down, just cutting out. I went to those therapy sessions seeking something that didn't exist. It is no wonder I didn't find it!

Sad to say, digging into my past just brought me pain and sadness, not the joy of release I was after. It was to be at least another ten years before I quit, once I'd worked out that the only way I could go was forwards. Before even embarking on that journey, I needed to work my way through a torrent of advice, a constant barrage concerning the harm that alcohol does us all. As if I didn't know!

Further adding to the problem, even though we know the harm alcohol does, we all have a little self-destruct button built into us. For me, when I was drinking, it was fully out there, on show to the world, and it would often get me into trouble. Familiar to anyone who has ever been tempted, there's a little voice whispering into your ears – and it's a bugger to control! It simply will not shut up.

And its name?

The EAF (aka the Fuck it Fairy)

So, what is the EAF?

Well, it's not a cousin of the BFG (Big Friendly Giant). Instead, the EAF is simply the Evil Alcohol Fairy. This little bastard also goes by the name of John Barleycorn, or to others, the Fuck it Fairy. This is the name I give her, as it works best for me. Sitting inside your head or on your shoulder, wherever, the Fuck it Fairy is forever with the drinker and the quitter alike, and she's a devious and nasty piece of work.

During my drinking days, my Fuck it Fairy would get me into all sorts of trouble. Specifically, she really kicked in if I was suffering badly from the night before. As with many of us, I would resort to some sort of hair of the dog if I was feeling rough, trying to take the edge off the banging hangover and often uncontrollable shakes. Towards the end of the first drink and beginning of the second, I'd be starting to feel normal again, the dreadful nausea would be clearing and my appetite would start to return. Now would be the time to stop, take it easy and recover gently.

But in would step my Fuck it Fairy. I'd finish the second pint, knowing that the rest of my day was clear to do as I wished, now that I was feeling better and had no responsibilities. I would be slightly drunk, and inevitably I'd be, 'Oh fuck it, I'll just have one more then head home for a snooze. That sounds perfect.' Oh dear, and I'd be off again, generally going through another five or six pints before mid-late afternoon and ruining another day.

Other times, during my drinking days, my Fuck it Fairy would turn a good day bad. For instance, I'd always go to the pub after playing a game of hockey – the whole team

45

would do. We'd have a bite to eat, typically sausage, chips and beans, and share a drink with the opposition. Most people would then drift away home at this point and get on with their afternoons and evenings. I'd always stay and have another drink, promising I'd call home and let my wife know I was running late. Then I'd look at the time and know I was in trouble.

'Fuck it! If I was going to be in trouble anyway I might as well make the most of it and have a few more beers!' Sound familiar? Bloody Fuck it Fairy taking over again, destroying all sense of reason, obligation and decency and taking advantage of my drunken state.

Once I was drunk, my Fuck it Fairy led me down all sorts of paths I'd never consider when sober. My sense of perspective was ruined, my fear was laid waste. I put myself in danger, and consequences were never considered. My Fuck it Fairy had my worst interests at heart, and became stronger and stronger as I became more and more inebriated.

Not that I got rid of her when I stopped drinking. She still calls to me, especially in my weakest moments, like a bully, taunting me, tempting me, confusing me. But her call is getting weaker by the day.

Each of our Fuck it Fairies will do all in her power to get us drinking again, and she will also call on the help of others. She will work away relentlessly to get us to question our decision to quit. Our friends may come out with statements like 'One glass won't hurt' or 'It's not like it's forever, is it?' and she'll latch on to these. We will have to listen to her, for the Fuck it Fairy will become louder at these points. She'll encourage us to come out with, 'Oh go on then, just the one' or 'Yeah I'm just trying to cut down, really'. She is the antithesis of willpower.

Our friends don't want to see us as different, our Fuck it Fairy wants us to keep on drinking, and if we are low on strength to resist at the end of the day, the result is almost inevitable. She will win, nine times out of ten.

Using willpower to beat her is always going to fail. She is strong and devious and has had years of practice working her way into our subconscious. On the other hand, if we are only starting to get used to using our willpower, it's an uneven contest from the start. Somehow, we need to tell her to fuck off herself. Using willpower will work for a while, but not forever. We need to kill her before she kills us, which she will.

Our Fuck it Fairy thrives on doubt. Doubt that you really want to quit. Doubt that you believe you can quit. Doubt that you are strong enough. Doubt that your friends will believe you. Doubt that life will actually be better without drinking. Each and every one of these doubts feeds the fairy, making her grow stronger.

So how do we kill her, free ourselves of her evil clutches? There is only one way; we must starve her. We must cut off her food, immediately and permanently. We can't make her smaller or less powerful by putting her on a diet, feeding her less doubt. We must remove all doubt and starve her, without delay. To do this we must make the decision, with total conviction, that we will never drink again, that we are, from now on in, a non-drinker (not even an ex-drinker, but a *non*-drinker).

This distinction is key because society does not expect a non-drinker to drink. It does expect an ex-drinker to drink because it has seen so many ex-drinkers start again. Non-drinkers never started in the first place. Be like them; they do not pine for something they never had. Do not pine, have no doubts, and you will starve your Fuck it Fairy. Without a drop, she will shrivel and die, and as you're now a non-drinker you will not be able to revive her, because in order for her to come back to life, she needs a drink. Starving her of doubt will kill her. Alcohol will revive her. This is why you must become a non-drinker, not an ex-drinker. That is too risky.

Willpower will help you make the decision and stick to it. Once that decision is made with absolute certainty, your fairy will soon be dead and you'll not need to call on willpower again. And as we'll soon discover, willpower can be a fickle friend, so it's best to keep it that way.

Otherwise, she'll soon be back.

In the doghouse

'I'm already in so much trouble, I might as well keep drinking.'

That's how I used to think anyway. I knew when I'd be in trouble with my wife for getting home late and drunk, so I used to think, *I may as well be really late and really drunk.* If I was going to be in the doghouse, I might as well have some fun beforehand, make the most of it. This, of course, although I didn't know it at the time, was my Fuck it Fairy finding her feet, flexing her muscles, getting ready for bigger battles ahead.

I recall friends saying that I really ought to get home, that it just wasn't worth it. They were handing me a key to safety, security and happiness, but I never recognised it for what it was. These were friends I was drinking with, those that might carry on drinking after I'd gone. I didn't want to miss out on that. They were not keeping me out, I was. And they had real concern for me. I guess they gave up in the end and, as I eventually headed home, they'd wish me luck.

Thank goodness those days are over.

But why on earth would a usually sensible man abandon all sense of reason like that and chose beer and trouble over peace? It simply makes no sense at all. I was constantly making a bad decision, and this very same one would be repeated time and time again. I knew that I was heading for deeply troubled waters as I decided to have another beer rather than go home, but still I'd choose the beer.

Reflecting on those days, I realise I was still a child, immature in so many ways. I was happy enough at work and at home, but still had that 'rules are there to be broken' mentality of a youngster. Even today, I feel that is still there in me, it's a part of who I am. This is my Fuck it Fairy.

Those drinking episodes were generally restricted to Saturdays, and only ever after playing hockey. At university, hockey had been a game very much associated with drinking, and I loved both. Once out of university and playing at home, I carried on with the drinking theme.

There was another very heavy drinker in the club and we bonded, both socially and alcoholically. This delighted me, of course, and I made sure the relationship flourished. I now had a partner in crime, and as this chap was such a massive drinker, I found that my heavy consumption paled into insignificance against his, so I felt much better about it. Was this man a bad influence on me? Not a bit of it. He couldn't care less if I was drinking water or wine, so long as he had a beer. I simply used him and his drinking habit as a cloak under which I could feel better about my own consumption.

At the time, I was in one of my bigger drinking phases, and thoroughly enjoying it. I'd had my gap year drinking, my university drinking, and was now in my late 20s, pre-family drinking phase. Other phases would come later, right through to my 50s, and the pattern would remain the same.

But, coming back to the question, why did I carry on drinking even when I knew I would get in some kind of trouble?

It comes down to the simple fact that alcohol strips us of our dignity and our ability to reason. We think only of ourselves, and consequences don't come into it. Why else would I have ended up, the only white man in an exclusively black club, alone, staggering home from a Christmas party?

I was so out of place, but at the time I didn't care! I wanted to hear some reggae, that was all that mattered. Was I in danger? Quite possibly. Did I care or even notice? No.

Alcohol removes our natural and necessary defences and leaves us vulnerable, whilst at the same time making us feel like a superhero. It's a lethal combination; we end up putting ourselves in danger, voluntarily. We almost seek it out. It is not our natural behaviour, as alcohol hijacks our reason and locks it away. As each drink passes our lips, reason fades further and further into the background until it is totally gone, replaced by bravado and, let's be honest, stupidity.

Only a stupid man would decide on another few beers and a bollocking from his wife rather than a peaceful life. Only an idiot spends a whole year living in a beautiful city, Chester, and is able to remember just ONE sober Saturday morning there. Only a fool puts himself in real physical danger. But once we take a drink, that is the person we can become. It was certainly the person I became. It may not be just the doghouse we end up in.

It could be prison, the hospital and, for some, the mortuary.

Somehow, I was lucky, I avoided all three. Looking back at some of the situations I got myself into, all three have beckoned me at some point, and more than just the once. Reading that back, the phrase 'that's a sobering thought' comes to mind. Taking that thought and turning it into action has made all the difference to my life. No longer do I awake with the potential that the day could end with me in one of those three places.

I do still end up in the doghouse from time to time, but these days it's when I don't clean the bathroom, or when I tread mud through the hallway from my filthy trainers. Much better. Once a fool, always a fool, but now a sober fool!

Back in the day, short-term pleasure from beer outweighed the long-term risk of trouble in the doghouse. The consequences were, so to speak, of no consequence!

When will I feel normal again?

That was it, short-term pleasure and long-term suffering. Somehow I'd decided that this was a fair balance, but that couldn't go on forever. After some time living this way, I recall standing outside my back door, looking over my narrow garden and thinking to myself, *When will I ever feel normal again?* I was in my mid-30s, years into feeling this way, now with a young daughter and a baby on the way. It was a time when I'd expect to be tired, working hard, life pretty much upside down, and with a new and expanding family.

But as I stood there with a numb head, drawing on yet another cigarette, all I could think was, *When will this end? I'm always so tired and sick.* I'd spent years surviving, barely getting on at work. Promotions? Yeah, right! But I was reasonably comfortable. Nothing more than that.

As for feeling normal again, I just wanted to have some energy, not feel stuffed up all the time, not be constantly drained and lacking in enthusiasm. With young children, I was expected to feel this way all the time, wasn't I? Sleepless nights, month after month, and looking after a toddler with a hangover was enough to send anyone over the edge. The thing is that I would always manage to find time for a drink, and I felt that I had at least earned it and deserved it after helping look after my daughter.

I can't believe that's what it was like. I was a father and rewarded myself with booze when I did something with the children. That's basically what I did, and anyone who flops down on the sofa after playing with their young children, and then cracking a beer or whatever, is doing exactly the same thing.

Even then I knew I should stop drinking, I knew I had a problem, but then wasn't the time to stop. After all, I'd be out of the twilight zone of baby and toddler sleeping patterns soon enough, and then I'd feel that much better, and able to cope with quitting.

In my 20s, and in the early years of marriage, I'd really only have a drink at the weekends. I was starting off in life, had got through the silly drinking years at university, and I'd maybe have the odd night with a midweek beer, but I didn't get drunk. I guess life was pretty normal back then.

Rolling forwards into my 30s, things began to unravel, as I can see now. My friends started having families, as did I. They settled down, I drank more. They seemed to become more and more responsible, I was heading in the other direction. Each day I was starting to feel less and less like normal. Outwardly, all was well, nothing was visible, and I was functioning at a reasonably responsible level. Inside I was sick and twisted. I wanted to get on, I wanted to be normal, not get poisoned all the time for no reason. I started drinking to feel normal again and never did. I was beginning to chase an illusion, and I knew it deep down.

I had to carry on though. To feel normal, I drank, and then I felt bad, ill, tired, and would castigate myself for it. I needed to feel normal again to be able to face quitting, but to get to a point where I felt normal required me to have a drink. I was well and truly stuck.

I stayed stuck for around 20 years, and my life basically went on hold. I didn't progress at work, at home, anywhere. I stopped growing. And all I could ask myself was, *When will I feel normal again?* I reasoned with myself that the day I felt normal would be the day I could quit, that that was all it would take. The only problem was that my standard feeling was low and tired, and in order to get up and running I'd have a drink. Decades of decay meant that I needed to have a drink to set myself up, to feel like I was on top of the world, or at least of myself.

I couldn't see what needed to happen for looking. I thought that I needed to feel a particular way to set my quit going. I also found, those days, that the only way I could approach feeling what I envisaged as normal was to drink. The truth of the matter was always staring me in the face:

I couldn't wait until I felt normal in order to quit, and I needed to quit in order to feel normal.

Was I going insane?

As I've just said, I couldn't wait until I felt normal in order to quit, so I'd find a way of forcing normal back on myself, by way of drinking.

Hair of the dog.

Think about it.

Why did I feel so shitty? Why was I sick? Why could I not face the day?

Because I'd drunk too much alcohol a few hours ago, that's why.

My cure? My remedy of choice?

Drink more alcohol.

Seriously? I got sick by drinking poison and I expected the same poison to make me well again? What is this miraculous alcohol? It works wonders!

No! It gets you drunk. The more you have the worse you feel afterwards, and the worse you feel afterwards the more you want it to make you feel better again! Wow! Look, this isn't aversion therapy where we cure people with a fear of heights by taking them up a tall building and increasing their confidence, this is alcoholism. Trying to make yourself, a drinker, better by drinking more is like turning a hose on a drowning man; it's only going to make things worse than they are.

So why did I do it?

I did it because my body, like yours, needs to maintain or return to a state known as homeostasis. In case you haven't come across this word before, it's a fancy name for balance. Think of it as Little Bear's porridge: it's 'just right'; or in the biological sense, it's that state of steady internal, physical and chemical systems that keep us stable.

Homeostasis is maintained by all living creatures to allow them to function optimally. This will include body temperature, fluid levels, nutrient intake and waste disposal, and it all occurs at cellular, organ and whole body levels. For instance, our kidneys work to maintain bodily homeostasis by regulating our salt and water levels. When we are in a state of homeostasis we feel and function at our best.

You may now be wondering what this has to do with hair of the dog, where one is a deeply complex and scientific biological process and the other a drunk's answer to a hangover. Let's just say that drinking hair of the dog is the best and most obvious response in this situation. By demanding the hair of the dog, our ancient brain is giving us the best way it knows in which we can return to a feeling of homeostasis. Put it like this: when I have drunk this way, I always had the following thought going through my mind:

I just want to feel normal again.

And from deep within, based on experience, our ancient survival system kicks in and says, 'Drink alcohol. It will stop you feeling so bad, it will get you back to a state where you feel much more comfortable, it will help you on your way to feeling normal again.' Hair of the dog is the body's quickest route back to homeostasis. Our instinct is acting to return us to normal. It may be flawed and seemingly illogical, but that is what it is doing. It is doing its best to keep us alive.

When you strip everything away from it, drinking hair of the dog is a survival mechanism, aimed at returning us to optimal functioning. It may be deeply flawed, but when faced with a choice between equilibrium and imbalance, even life and death, logic doesn't come into it; we are driven to keep alive right now. What matters for survival is happening now, not next year when the effects of a further year's drinking are being realised. We need to be well now, because we are alive now. The future doesn't exist and so it doesn't feature in our unconscious survival decision-making process.

So rather than our being insane by drinking hair of the dog, it is, in fact, exactly what we need to do. We just need to make sure we don't get there in the first place, and we'll not need to face it again.

Drinking this way does return us to a more comfortable place, albeit briefly. Over time, we gradually decline if we continue down this path. Quitting returns us to a more comfortable place. Over time, we gradually continue feeling better and better if we go this way instead.

It's a way of life

In general, and I'm sure it's common across most drinkers, I was on the lookout for excuses or reasons to drink. I would anticipate events for weeks on end, knowing there would be a perfect excuse to have a guilt-free drink coming up. Maybe it would be a barbeque with friends, a family get together, or going to a rugby match with my wife. Even then I'd make sure I got a few in; it was rugby, after all. I had to have a few!

So, I would often use excitement as a precursor to drinking, and I'd use the event itself as the reason and excuse to drink. As a drinker, any excuse would do. I could drink for any reason, even the days of the week:

- Friday – woohoo, end of the week!
- Sunday – boohoo, end of the weekend!
- Wednesday – yay, halfway there!

And that doesn't involve any emotion, that's just making it up to make me feel better inside. I needed to drink, so now, three days a week, I could justify it. *Result!* as they say.

Maybe I'd had an awful day at work – drink. A great day at work – drink. A day at work – drink. Bad traffic on the way home, a disagreement with anyone, simply feeling tired – drink, drink, drink. Whatever was going on, a drink was justified, even needed. And then, even when there was nothing going on, I'd have to have a drink for that very reason – to fill the time when there was nothing going on. Come what may, I never just drank, there was always a reason I could find. It was always justified. By finding a justification for every drink I had, I was really just pushing the guilt away, keeping it at bay for as long as possible.

But perhaps the worst of my drinking came when I was feeling down. I could feel down in two ways, one physically and one emotionally. If I was tired, I'd run out of steam and was just drained, then I would simply vegetate and drink. If I was feeling blue, then I would drink to delete the feeling. I never did find the answer at the bottom of the glass, but, as you'll know, by the time we've got there we'll have forgotten what the question was anyway. Which is kind of the point.

It was in one such glum state that I hit perhaps my lowest ebb. I'd lost my mother a week or so earlier, so wasn't exactly feeling chirpy. I really found the funeral service quite hard in many ways, and was glad to be out of the church, and away from the crematorium as well. We all gathered in the village hall afterwards for drinks and nibbles, and I'd been put in charge of sourcing and laying out the drinks – 'sale or return' from my local supermarket. I can't believe just how much I'd ordered in, although looking back it was always going to be a great way to ensure I had a few weeks' supply of wine in the house afterwards. There certainly wasn't going to be any 'return' purchases. On the day of the funeral, there was enough wine and beer to fell a small army, and there were about 60 of us in all. I hate to admit it, but I hit the booze big time. A bit was to settle me down, but as soon as I was up and running I was in drinking mode, not funeral mode. I got into a terrible state, and I now know that I used the emotional turmoil card as an excuse to go over the top. I used my own mother's death as a pass to get drunk. I'd even booked the next day off work in anticipation of this – I wasn't stupid! Or was I?

I'm not recounting this with any sort of pleasure, but just to show how very warped my thinking had become in those days, to even think that this was an acceptable way to behave. It now fills me with horror, but that was then and I can't turn back the clock and live it any differently. For me, the past can stay right there; it is no more. I lost all sense of dignity that day, which was unforgivable, and now that I have stopped drinking I am regaining that dignity, behaving in a manner that we would term as civilised. It's a much better way to be, in control, balanced and behaviourally acceptable.

Reflecting on such occasions may be hard, but remember: they are in the past and can't be altered. When thinking of your own aberrations, try not to dwell on them, but recognise them for what they *were*: a reflection of who you *were*, and not who you are and want to be. That way you'll keep progressing towards, or in, your quit.

While drinking, I truly believed that I had to drink to get through life, that it was an essential part of it. The fear of never drinking again brought up so many questions about the future. These were all along the lines of:

- How can I socialise without a drink?
- What will people think of me?
  (I'll be labelled something I don't like.)
- Will my friends abandon me?
- Christmas, New Year? Surely not!

Because I had spent my entire life going through all these situations, for as long as I could remember, drunk, I couldn't conceive of how I could get through them without a drink. There was no way I could imagine a night out at the local and listening to a band without a few beers. That just wasn't how things went, was it? I was spinning up visions of how my friends would treat me, almost laugh at me, certainly leave me well alone. Indeed, what's the point of going out and not drinking?

I feared a life I had never experienced, and I feared what other people would think. If I was to stop drinking, I'd lose my identity, expose myself without any armour, and that was an uncomfortable thought. The true me, hidden behind a façade of alcohol for so long, would come out, and I'd have to live with him forever.

But most of all, I believed that I'd miss my true friend and ally, alcohol itself. It had got me through good times and bad. It may have let me down from time to time, but it was always there, like a loyal dog. I knew I could rely on it to help me escape, take me to another place; and at the time, I truly believed I enjoyed being drunk, and spent every evening that way. I was afraid that, without alcohol, I would be unable to enjoy myself, have friends and relax.

I was afraid of stopping, of losing all that, of never being able to drink again.

I was equally afraid of continuing, of drinking forever, of losing everything: my family, health, job, everything. How many times I set a stop date in my head I don't know; there were hundreds. But as soon as they arrived, there would be something to keep me drinking. Even just the thought of stopping was enough to make me drink again!

I couldn't imagine a life without drink (or one that was any good anyway), and at the same time I feared drinking it all away. I was stuck, frozen, so I did nothing year after year. No fight, no flight, nothing changed. It was easier that way, simply ignoring my fears, and truly believing that, one day, I'd be OK. That glimmer of hope of quitting, without any real chance of it actually happening, kept me going. It gave me hope and involved no effort. And that meant I kept drinking, which is what I really wanted anyway. Because I felt I couldn't function properly without, I needed alcohol just to get by.

Two messy days

Many people use alcohol to enhance a situation, or at the very least to make a great day even greater. In the end, it rarely works, with such days ending in a mess.

Let's look at a couple of such days. They were a number of years and many miles apart, and each led directly to my quit. The first was a trip to Lord's; the second, a pub crawl around the villages of south Northamptonshire.

The night before heading to Lord's, travelling by train, I'd had a few beers. I don't know why, but I was really suffering badly in the morning, much more so than I should have been. Thus, to help myself get through the journey I'd bought a couple of cans of beer at the train station to have on the way up to London. Sipping my way through Wolverton, Milton Keynes Central, Tring and Watford Junction, these cans worked pretty well, and by the time the train pulled into Euston Station I was feeling just about OK.

As was the arrangement, my brother would provide the food for the day and I'd look after the drinks. Recently, we'd always had a few when we met up for cricket, so I stocked up with five or six bottles of wine and one of champagne. (I later told the man at the entry gate that I was providing for a party of six and I got in, no problem.)

So, with a bag full of drinks and an hour still to go, I decided to get the happy day started with a quiet pint and watch the world go by, and so I did. By around 10:30am I was three pints down and feeling relaxed, ready for a day of chatting and watching some great cricket. By 11:30am the champagne was gone, and by 12:30pm we were getting stuck into the second bottle of wine. This was going to be a long day and as my brother was also nursing a hangover, drinking them away together was the obvious solution.

Conversation flowed, we laughed, we drank, we laughed again, and drank some more.

The beers were making it into a fun and somewhat raucous occasion. As is the way at Lord's, we soon went for a walk to see who else was about (it's not all about watching cricket), catch up with some old friends, speak to whoever happened to be there. Falling in with a rum bunch, we found ourselves eating a formal lunch, prime lamb, plenty of wine and chatter. It was turning into a fantastic and memorable day.

Fast-forward a couple of hours, and I knocked a bottle of wine over, sending it rolling, slow-motion, over the edge of the stairwell in front of where I was sitting, only to fall and whack an official ground steward on the head! Accident, yes. Caused by drunkenness, certainly. I was mortified. Fortunately, he was cool about it. How he was I'll never know! Next up, my brother somehow managed to take a wrong turn on the way back from the loo and ended up on the playing surface (absolutely forbidden!), only to be escorted off by the security staff. He wasn't ejected from the ground, but was rightly and hugely embarrassed.

We'd both made fools of ourselves at the home of cricket, in front of thousands, but as I recall we simply laughed it off, cracked another bottle and carried on as normal. We acted like nothing happened! As for the rest of the day, I don't even recall leaving the ground, making my way across London, getting the train back to Northampton, or arriving home. I'd set out to have a great day watching cricket. I'd ended up getting very, very drunk, unable to recall any of the game itself, the conversations I'd had or the people we'd seen. Drinking was to be a part of the day, something to enhance it; to make a happy occasion or a good feeling, even better. Instead, as I don't have an off switch, that good feeling, that enhancement, lasted about

20 minutes (the first two glasses in the morning), and then gradually got more and more blurry and unbalanced. Rather than being an emotional stimulant and partner, alcohol took everything away that day. I'd started the day with a light hangover, with a drink, and all I'd done was kept going.

Two years or so later, and another hangover was upon me, but this time, rather than drink myself out of it, I spent an hour at my local bootcamp. I was starting the day with fresh air and exercise. I was earning my forthcoming beer! Not only that, and even at the age of 53, I was genuinely looking forward to seeing my friends for a fun afternoon of sun and beer, and so I was trying to accelerate the morning. I wasn't accelerating it so I could get to see them sooner, I know that. I just knew that the sooner I saw them, the sooner we'd be in the pub, a rare occasion when I could drink all day without feeling guilty. Even better, I knew that my wife and children would be away the next day, so I was under no pressure for the next morning. I could relax into the day. I was emotionally excited and also chilled. I could do as I pleased, and so I did.

By the time we reached pub number five or six (we stayed in some for a few drinks, others just the one), I was sneaking the odd extra drink for myself whilst ordering a round for everyone else. I'd also hit upon the idea that 4:00pm shots were a good idea, although this was not one shared particularly enthusiastically by everyone else! There was no theme to the day, just lads and beers, so I went for it much more than in previous years. I don't know why. I drank to blackout, had absolutely no idea where or when the day ended when I retired to bed or where I was when I woke. I was at least undressed, in a bed, and with my clothes in a heap next to me. Was I put there or did I manage that myself? I don't know, and I sure as heck wasn't going to ask.

I got up and out of the house as fast as my legs would carry me. What had I said? What had I done yesterday and last night? I didn't want to know. I'd been drinking to make me feel more excited, happy, with friends, and I'd gone too far. Again.

I was so sad, sick and hungover that I parked up outside my house, dropped my bag inside and headed straight to the pub. I was in an emotional storm and needed to find calmer waters, so I did what I knew would help me, and quickly, I drank. I intended to have just two, then sleep it off before the family came home. Hours later, they were home, and I was still in the pub.

As I put my beer glass down, for the last time before going home, I knew it would be my last drink ever. I had made a promise to myself and this time it felt different. Everywhere in my body and soul knew I would never drink again. There could be no more drinking; I'd reached the end.

I had drunk to be happy, drunk to be sad, drunk to forget and to cure, all in the space of 24 hours. Not one of those drinks had done what it promised and I knew it never could. I was done with alcohol before my head hit the pillow. That was many months ago now, and I've not been tempted to have a drink even once since then.

Drinking wrought havoc with my emotions even as I believed it would enhance the good and quash the bad. Putting it down has brought calm and happiness. The lies that alcohol tells no longer suck me in.

Am I immune? Who knows, but I'm no longer drinking! And I used to drink for any and every reason.

Whilst I had remained in two minds about quitting I either drank, or suffered so much stress and angst when I was not drinking, that neither was doing me any good. All my life I had been shown images and heard all about how great drinking is. Bombarded from birth, you will no doubt have experienced some of these 'benefits' during your drinking career as well. We have all had great experiences where alcohol has been involved. Alcohol will have enhanced situations, acted as an ice-breaker. Without these there would be no good news stories, alcohol would have no real appeal. It would be totally crazy of me to suggest that we haven't had a good time, probably many, when we were drinking alcohol.

It is these good times, coupled with images, advertisements, stories of other people having a good time, that has set our brains to a 'booze is good' mode. Whilst this may be true for a certain period of our lives there comes a point when the balance flips, and alcohol starts causing more harm than good. If we drink enough of an addictive poison, regardless of how well it is dressed up as craft beer or botanical gin, it will poison us. It isn't that this change happens overnight; it often creeps up on us and before we know it, we wake one day and realise there's a problem. It's often the case that other people, your friends and family, will see this before you do – but nobody's going to say anything, are they? By the time this happened to me, the problem had its claws well and truly embedded in me. I just could not see it happening. Or I ignored it.

It is now that we start to think about the harm that drinking is doing us. We become very aware of the mental, physical and social harm it does. I certainly became super-aware, I couldn't stop seeing alcohol absolutely everywhere I looked. Once I realised I had a problem, I became super-sensitive to alcohol all round me. My brain, programmed with the 'booze is good' message, was now picking up messages containing alcohol more and more than ever before. This simply added fuel to that fire.

I also knew, and became increasingly knowledgeable about, the damage it does. I saw this damage all around me as well. I saw drunks on the street, news articles about alcohol-fuelled abuse, drink-drive campaigns and so on. These were all very well, but they were external to me. They didn't resonate. I was not a street drinker, slugging vodka from a brown paper bag and sleeping in a shop front. I had a decent job, a fantastic wife and children and went on nice holidays. We had a shiny new car, big house and didn't beat each other up. I wasn't a drink-driver; that scared me. All the images and stories were about what happened to other people. I wasn't like that, and so the messages I was receiving simply didn't make an impact on the ingrained 'booze is good' message.

Thus, I was living a contradiction. One part of me was telling me booze was good, but experience was telling me it wasn't any more. One half saw that booze was bad, but only ever recognised or accepted that in other people. At this point we have not only a drink problem, but a mental problem. By mental problem, I absolutely don't mean a mental illness or fault, but a problem that needs solving, and can be solved, like a puzzle.

The problem we have is that our brain sees, and then believes and experiences, two different things at the same time, and both are right. Whilst we hold this pattern of opposites as true, together, where there can only actually be one truth, we will not be able to quit. We will always see the good in drinking, no matter how bad things become. In fact, when things get really bad, drinking becomes even more attractive, not less so.

With alcohol, our life simply gets worse. When we spend time not drinking, life is pretty good, but we don't put that down to an absence of drink, at least not at the deeper level where the 'booze is good' message is stored.

This contradiction we live with is something that must be eradicated if we are to quit. So let us turn and look, briefly, at what we need to do to achieve this. In simple terms, we need to turn ourselves into a successful person, but only successful at ONE single thing. Not drinking.

But how to do that? Have a good look around you at successful people you know, you see on TV, read about in books and newspapers. What makes them all successful is one single thing, far more important than intellect, natural ability or education. That one single thing is hard work, backed up by dedication and practice. They have all set their eyes on a prize and gone after it. Their paths may not have been direct. They will have had failures and setbacks on the way, but they will never have given up. They will have listened and learned, taken things on board and acted on them. They will have repeated what worked and abandoned what didn't.

Do this with your quitting journey, and soon enough your 'booze is good' belief will fade. It will turn out to be no more permanent than a kid's temporary tattoo you get from bubble-gum wrappers! Learn, practise and embed whatever works for you. Not every successful person became that way by following the same path as their predecessors; they found their own path. Likewise, your quit will be your own. You will piece it together with bits of this and bobs of that.

And then, one day, your brain will no longer see that 'booze is good'. You will no longer have that contradiction in your mind; the conflict will be over. At that point you can put down the drink, with little or no effort, and certainly with no stress, and your quit will start.

You will now be one of those successful people. And it feels good!

'Fat, sick and nearly dead'

Put another way, I was sick and tired of feeling sick and tired. I had reached the end of the line with living this way.

For over 20 years I'd been throwing excess alcohol down my neck. I'd had the oddest experiences mixing whisky and Baileys, peeing out of friends' bedroom windows into the vicar's garden next door. I'd vomited in alleyways on Tuesday evenings and slept in Cornish ditches after an argument with my tent mates. I had seen people near to me suffer, even die, as a direct result of drinking alcohol either over time or in one big session. My own family had its famous '60 Capstan Full Strength and a bottle of port a day' survivor, and even members of my own generation aren't escaping from the clutches of alcohol.

Deciding to quit was to get out of this never-ending lifestyle. It got to the point when I felt my best for about 20 minutes a day, somewhere between starting my second drink and my fourth. Before the first I would be shaking, quite literally, finding it difficult to swallow (that was the oddest thing and really quite frightening), and with a body as tense as the steels on the Bristol Suspension Bridge. I actually felt physically tight, rigid, as if I were about to snap. This wasn't in my mind. This was in my muscles, my sinews and tendons, and it was a horrible feeling. I don't know how I didn't pass out; that feeling of hypertension was awful.

Once the second drink had made its way down my throat, I felt totally relaxed, at ease and could not care less. Discomfort had been banished with that drink, and I had restored a balance within my body and my mind. I didn't care and nor did it even cross my mind that this balance was based on the actions of a lethal poison. It was the result that mattered, and the result was good. Once past this and onto the third and fourth drinks, with my body feeling good, I could swallow again, and thoughts of what was to come the next day would be gone. Living in that moment of carefree drunkenness was what I needed. It was my go-to place when I was drinking.

I truly believed that gentle to mild intoxication was perfect, and that I enjoyed it. Each day, that feeling would last around 20 minutes and I believed I was content. Maybe I actually was, but the issue was that I was either drunk or hungover for the remaining 23 hours and 40 minutes of every day. Even my sleep was ruined with having to wake in the night, suffering 3:00am panic attacks, and waking soaked from the sweats.

I was never a big man, but I had grown a belly and was getting heavier. My eyes drooped, hammock-like bags below each, and I could see the signs of thread-like veins appearing on my face. My skin was starting to get blotchy in places, and my stools were anything but firm. I was starting to see the outward effects of what I was doing to myself. Having a drink helped push these sights to the back of my mind. I didn't even think what I must look like inside, but I knew how it felt.

All the time I was feeling well below par, and the only way I knew to get back up to level was to drink alcohol. I knew it would be temporary, and I also knew it would work. History had proven that, and thus I was safe in the knowledge that, come what may, alcohol would take away the feeling of being 'fat, sick and nearly dead'.

A couple of times towards the end, including my last day drinking, it actually didn't work, and I knew I was in trouble. The second drink didn't take the edge away, I still felt tense inside, and my swallowing reflex was still not working. All I could do was drink even more. The thumping headache of a hangover is usually sorted by getting drunk again, but with each beer it got worse. I knew I was in trouble. I was fat, I was sick, and I was approaching the nearly dead phase. Not only was I now sick and tired of feeling sick and tired, I was starting to get frightened. To suppress this fear, I resorted to type, and drank. Slowly but surely the decision to quit was being made for me, as I approached a fork in the road.

I could see the fork coming for quite some time, and I had been putting it off time and time again. In one direction I was to carry on drinking. Life would continue to deteriorate, my health would fail and I would die an uncomfortable death. I drank when I looked at that fork as it scared me and anyway, that would never happen to me! The other fork would be to a life of sobriety, but I struggled to see beyond simply not drinking.

I guess I was also lucky as it came closer and closer to the point where I had no choice but to decide which fork in the road I was to take. By then I had tried Alcoholics Anonymous (AA), Allen Carr and therapy. I had read and re-read various books and studies on the subject of alcohol and quitting. I'd also had experience of quitting an addictive drug, having been a heavy smoker for years and quitting some time ago. It wasn't that by doing any of this that I had managed to quit drinking, but I had a very good understanding and appreciation of what it was all about, what to do and what to avoid. I was fully equipped, and had succeeded before.

On the weekend of 16th-17th September 2019, I had my last drink. A friend had sat with me, towards the end of the day, and we talked. Finally, I put an empty beer glass down on the table. It was 4:40pm and I'd been drinking all day. I walked home, went to bed and haven't had a drink since.

I had reached the end of my tether. I knew I was in deep trouble, that alcohol had stopped working for me, and was now working against me in every single aspect of my life. Not one part of me, my conscious brain, my unconscious brain, my body, my anything, could see of any benefit in drinking any more. I had worked my way through it all, and at the end of the road there was no fork. The road that led to continued drinking now had a 'No entry' sign on it, and that was that.

It was a blessed relief, and I could step off the crazy train at last.

WHERE IT ALL STARTS

A new discovery

Imagine this. The world has been around for millennia. Humankind has been thriving for 10,000 years since the last Ice Age. We have changed from being hunter-gatherers to lawyers and accountants. Now living in huge numbers across the globe, we also have wonderful medicines and drugs that can halt measles, smallpox has been all but eradicated, and we are starting to control malaria. This is a great time to be alive. Life expectations have risen in terms of both quality and length, with people living healthily into their '70s and '80s, often well beyond.

People enjoy a massive variety of food and drink from across the globe; they are almost spoilt for choice. Sports, the arts, literature and science are all thriving and, for the most part, people live harmoniously.

Taking a walk around this world, you notice there are no pubs or off-licences. There are no drunks on the street. There are no groups of young men rolling home, singing bawdy songs on a Saturday night, intimidating passers-by. Hospital waiting rooms are not heaving with bruised and battered 20-somethings after a weekend punch-up. There are no police patrols pulling drivers over after an evening out as Christmas approaches, checking they are safe to drive – because they all are.

Is this Utopia? I don't know. But just recently a scientist has discovered a new substance. She has found that by allowing vegetable matter to rot, mixing it up with some other chemicals and herbs, she can make an incredible new drink that not only tastes OK, but also changes the state of the drinker's mind. She has discovered alcohol. This has never been seen in the world and the scientist thinks she may just have made the discovery of the century. If only she could sell it, she would be rich beyond her wildest dreams.

All the scientist has to do is get the relevant approvals from the various government agencies and so on, and she's good to go. And, as this wonderful substance affects the mind – this is perhaps its most appealing characteristic – it will count as a drug. Like any other drug coming out in this world, much like our own, Utopia has a strict policy of testing for safety.

So the scientist sets forth on a two-pronged mission. First, she works to get her new discovery approved for public use, and second, she works on a sales strategy.

Let's look at the sales piece first. To sell her new drink into a market already brimming over with choice and variety, she needs to find something unique about hers. Of course, that's easier than you can imagine; it alters your state of mind. She's tried it out in secret with some friends and they all say that it's amazing. It really helps a party go with a bang, and they find life much more exciting, laughing and joking more than usual when they drink it. That has to be a good thing, right?

Focusing on her drink being one that makes a social occasion more fun, that it is also a life-enhancer, the scientist is loving the prospect of a change in direction in her life, and of wealth. No longer stuck in a lab, she's out promoting what she believes in, and is convinced she will make a fortune from it.

At the same time, government researchers are checking out the new drink, ensuring it is safe for public consumption. As we and the scientist understand, it needs to be treated it as a drug. The authorities need to make sure it does no harm, that it doesn't have any undesirable side-effects. After all, the last thing people want is to eat or drink something that will make them sick, either now or in the future. And like any new drug coming to market, this is what's being checked out.

During the course of the trial, numerous experiments are carried out, using alcohol and placebos, to understand the nature of this new drink/drug. The results start to come in almost immediately, and then over the longer term. As with medical trials today, they çan take five to ten years to complete, and only then is a drug approved for use. Imagine releasing a drug that caused harm. Nobody would want that horror situation, would they? Would you?

So as the results start coming in, the researchers start to get concerned. Symptoms and side-effects are worrisome. Here are some that they notice:

People in the trial can become aggressive. Others become withdrawn and morose. Their moods change substantially.

People lose their sense of balance. Their sight deteriorates. They find it difficult to operate simple tools or to follow simple instructions.

The deterioration continues to worsen the more of the substance they consume. Some people even vomit after drinking this new product.

Many participants complain of feeling ill the next day, suffering from headaches, nausea and physical shakes.

The trials are not looking promising, but continue. Over a period of months, a number of the participants on the trial start showing strange changes in their behaviour. It appears they start to desire this new drink; they are becoming addicted to it. At the same time, these are the same people who often show the poorest results in terms of physiological wellbeing. Strangely, those that are getting the sickest, over time, tend to want to consume more - *need* to consume more, according to all the feedback given in these controlled tests.

Sadly, a number of the triallists actually pass away, and post-mortem examinations show real damage has been done to their internal organs, unlike anything observed in the general population.

The trial ends, and the results are published. The conclusion is clear and unequivocal:

Unfit for human consumption.

Alcohol never even got off the ground. It was doomed from the start. Causing illness, disease and death, this new drug was never going to get approved. The scientist inventor would never get rich.

Only it didn't really happen that way, did it? If alcohol were discovered today, and you were asked to sign off regarding its safety, would you? Does this maybe change how you look at it? Maybe it strengthens your resolve to remove it from your life?

More harmful than any other drug known to man – more so than heroin, cocaine and crack (by combined numbers) – this drug is advertised everywhere, used by almost everyone, and can be bought cheaply and freely in the shop next door.

That's the world we inhabit, and through it we must navigate our lives.

Not only that, but also when the health impacts of alcohol are assessed, it's the dubious positives that attract all the attention, and we get headlines along the lines of 'The seven reasons why drinking red wine is good for you'.

Research – it's good for you!

When it comes to alcohol, it's not so much that there is fake news out there; rather it is that we are presented with a view that is out of line with reality. What I mean by this is that for every bad news story about the side-effects of alcohol, we are constantly bombarded by positive tales regarding the beneficial effects. The more we dig into this, the more interesting it gets.

But before we get started, let's just agree on some facts:

1. Alcohol is a poison.
2. Alcohol is a highly addictive drug.
3. Alcohol consumption leads to illness and often death.
4. If alcohol were discovered today, it would not be made legal. It would be classified along the lines of heroin and crack cocaine, a seriously harmful Class A drug.

I think we can all buy into these four truths, so we are all at the same starting point.

But enough of that. We all drink or drank alcohol in various quantities, we all take this drug without a second thought. So here goes, have a think about this next sentence:

If alcohol is a highly addictive drug, a poison, how can there be a safe limit on its consumption of a given number of units per week?

If it is poison, then surely a limit of none is appropriate? Or is a little bit of poison, OK? Maybe even good for us. That's what many would like us to think.

For example, we have all seen headlines along the lines that a glass of red wine a day is good for us. Just go online and search for the health effects of alcohol, and top of the list will come all the purported benefits. Not until you get further down will you start seeing the research on its harmful effects. Similarly, look through the newspapers and you'll find plenty of reports about the benefits of alcohol, and very few about its dangers.

Bad news doesn't sell copy.

Let's just spend a moment on the red wine issue. It's one we are all familiar with, I'm sure. The claim is that there is a chemical – resveratrol – in red wine that aids circulation. As a result of this finding, and with a nod to the fact that some people like a drink more than others, it is suggested we should drink one glass of red wine each day. Any more than that and the benefits are outweighed by the ill effects. We also know that nobody takes any notice of that bit, we all just see 'red wine is good for you' and take that away.

Indeed, if this were the only source of the magic chemical, then there may be something in that. Not surprisingly, when we dig a little deeper, we find that resveratrol is abundant in raspberries, blueberries and peanuts, as well as a host of other foods. We can get plenty of it that way, with no side-effects. But that's dull, it doesn't excite us in any way, and it certainly doesn't help red wine sales!

As I said above, look online and you'll see plenty of research and findings. Look more deeply into these and you'll be amazed at how these tests have been done. On the whole, those pieces of work done on the benefits of alcohol have two things in common:

1. There are very small sample sizes
2. The results are taken out of context.

Where we have very small sample sizes, we do not come across scientifically robust/valid or statistically significant results. They prove nothing, but the results can sound exciting, and someone will grab hold of them and promote them, for sure.

Second, results are often taken out of context. There may be some comments in a research paper that confirm a particular characteristic in alcohol (for instance, it may stop sufferers of x feeling y) and these are plucked out, expanded and made to look as if they are the main findings. This is often not the case and looking more deeply, these purported benefits are so heavily caveated that they recede into insignificance. Again, nobody is interested in that part of the research. Cherry-picking what appears to be good news is so much better.

We all know that alcohol is bad for us. We do not need to be reminded. What we do love to hear though is that it has health benefits. Set aside the facts, we could all do with a bit of good news from time to time. Moreover, what better news than drinking being of real benefit to you?

That's what these findings, over time and as they get more widespread, tell us, pure and simple. They may start as 'a daily glass of red wine is good for your circulation' but eventually turn into 'drinking is good for you'.

We may not think that, actively, but you can bet your bottom dollar on the fact that your primitive, survival brain has made that connection, cementing the benefits of drinking alcohol into your very being without your realising it has happened.

Finally, you will not be surprised to learn just how many of these pieces of 'good news research' are sponsored by the drinks companies. Most, if not all of them, are linked in one way or another. It's really just another piece of advertising, done very cleverly under the guise of scientific research.

With these credentials, which few people dispute, is it any surprise we are taken in? In general, we are all influenced by authority, and take what it says seriously (especially when we like the sound of what that authority is stating).

We pounce on it when we are told:

'Researchers' at "university" have found evidence that alcohol has benefits.'

That is some powerful advertising message, and we are all taken in by it.

It's nothing like the whole truth. Few of us look for that. When we do, we can see that we have been taken for a ride. None of us likes that either. Have a look, dig around, see what you can discover. I think you'll be surprised and will start looking at this topic from a totally different angle and, with any luck, this will help bring down the façade that surrounds alcohol.

Ultimately, understanding this will solidify your quit, make it that much easier to walk away from alcohol, and not want to drink it again.

Whilst we still believe in alcohol, we'll carry on handing over the cash, dutiful cash dispensers that we are. But how has it come to this?

A bit about advertising – or 'We've been had'

From the moment we are born we are bombarded with advertising of all sorts. Some is clear and obvious: TV, billboards, magazines. Some is less so: product placement in shows, discussions overheard. What they all have in common is they will work their way into our psyche, almost or actually unnoticed. And the longer we are exposed, the more the messages stick.

In this section we'll look at advertising in general, and then dig deeper into some specific messages to see what is going on and what we can maybe do about it. But first, let's consider what it's all about, in the most general terms.

Today, any producer or supplier has the ultimate aim of exchanging what they offer for money. Very rarely are swaps done, except maybe things like jobs and favours between friends. Rarely does this take place in the commercial world, and the supply of alcoholic drinks lives in the commercial world, not the world of swaps and favours. Producers of alcoholic drinks have something to sell, and we, the consumers, have money.

It is the aim of the producer to move that money from our pockets to theirs, and for that we get to consume their product. The product could be a shirt, a TV show, a bottle of wine, anything. Now, to fulfil that aim the producer will need to make that exchange look a good one, one we want to engage with.

And this is where advertising comes in. It will convince us to do something, and we will only ever do it if we are convinced it is a worthwhile thing, a fair exchange. So, how does this work?

The alcohol industry advertises by working on our deepest desires and emotions; in my opinion, it works on the very things that make us human beings. This is not so very different from other product advertising, but let's stick with booze here.

However, before we start looking at the way in which advertisers work, there's one very clear thing we should make ourselves aware of:

Alcohol advertising is everywhere.

Everywhere and all the time. Wherever we seem to look there is a poster, an image, a word spoken, a song lyric, even rubbish on the street (empty, crushed, beer cans), all alluding to alcohol. It invades every walk of life from sports sponsorship to health and wellness claims, from dramatic portrayals in soap operas to student rag weeks. We simply can't avoid it. And even if we don't actively notice all these sights and sounds, they are still being picked up in our subconscious mind and stored away in the filing cabinets of our brains. From birth. Or as near as, dammit.

Let's therefore turn our attention from the ubiquitous nature of alcohol advertising, to some specific examples, to some of the ways we are convinced (as if we need it) that we need to have a drink:

1. You are living an unfulfilled life.

A bit of a classic this one, the clear message is: 'Either you or I are lacking something' or it's 'Look what you could have if...'

2. You need to fit in.

Alcohol advertising often focuses on social acceptance, being part of a tribe. The clear message being put across is that if you drink this particular brand you will be included, have friends, be popular. I'll drink to that.

3. You'll have more fun.

Happy, smiling faces embarking on adventures have a certain appeal. We aspire to the same. Advertisers use this to promote sales.

4. You'll be healthier.

Although alcohol advertising can no longer make such claims, it did in the past, and we have long memories. Who can forget the line 'Guinness is good for you', or 'Heineken refreshes the parts other beers cannot reach'? The message? Alcohol makes you feel better. But does it?

These are just four obvious tactics. They are quite blatant and appeal to our base needs. This is why they are so successful, and explains why just about everyone accepts that alcohol is an important part of our lives. I understand that completely, but there are a number of us out here that find it hard to keep it that way, to keep it fun and social. For us, we need to be much more aware of what the advertisers are telling us, see through it and recognise what will happen if we drink.

We already know the answer, so defending ourselves against this onslaught should be a relatively simple thing, and comes down to maintaining a general awareness and questioning attitude. With that, we need not succumb to the purported attractions of drinking.

Sometimes though, this can be difficult because of the associations drinks companies make with healthy lifestyles, particularly when coupled with sports and adventure. After all, sponsorship is big business.

Sponsorship, sport and adventure

Guinness, Carling, Trivento, Talisker. Stout, lager, wine, whisky. Rugby Union, football, adventure sports, rowing.

Probably since the days of sponsorship being dreamt up, unhealthy foods and drinks have been associated with sport and physical prowess. Do we remember the furore over Coca-Cola and the Olympics? Coca-Cola, a sugar delivery mechanism, sponsoring the celebration of the greatest of all human physical achievements. Doesn't sound quite right, does it? But remember, money talks.

Just what is it that links drinking alcohol with sporting excellence? It's an interesting question, and one that goes to the heart of what it means to be human, to be accepted and to achieve something. Many of us like to watch sport, live or on TV. Others play themselves. Lots of people like to get out and about, into the countryside, the mountains. We love the camaraderie of an occasion shared.

We can do all these things without alcohol. Indeed, we are much better at them without alcohol. Wine is not a performance-enhancing drug when it comes to rock climbing, or any other activity for that matter. A large swig of premium lager between games does not improve our ability to play tennis (even though the last grass court tournament before Wimbledon, Queens, was once sponsored by Stella Artois). In every aspect of our life, the consumption of alcohol impairs our performance, so what's with the sports sponsorship?

There are two ways to look at this, one in terms of corporate affordability, the other in terms of human desire.

Taking corporate affordability first, we all recognise that the size of audience for various sports is large, with venues packing in thousands of supporters. There may also be millions watching on TV. To promote a product into this environment is of course hugely expensive, and only a few can afford it. Spending vast sums on advertising and promotion also has to be worth it. Nobody will spend millions, even tens of millions, without knowing there will be a healthy return on that investment.

For example, in the 2019 Superbowl, alcoholic drinks manufacturer AB Inbev spent a staggering $42 million on advertising. But then again, it's estimated that half of all US households tuned in and saw their commercial. That's a big audience.

With such huge audiences, advertising costs are enormous, and so only a very few organisations can afford it. This is the world of Big Tobacco, Big Pharma, Big Alcohol. These are the players here. Big Tobacco used to be a massive sporting sponsor from Formula 1 cars (JPS, Marlboro) to cricket (Benson and Hedges) and snooker (Embassy). That's now all over, as we have recognised the immense health issues around smoking and have banned advertising smoking and smoking-related products. And even though it could be argued that alcohol is a bigger health issue, this, the most dangerous drug known to man, is freely promoted across the globe as a partner to sport and physical prowess.

So, on corporate affordability, the drinks companies have deep pockets and are powerful lobbyists. With the consumption of alcohol being an integral part of many human societies, the drinks companies exploit this situation, as they are there to make money for their shareholders and owners.

Sport brings people together. It creates communities, engenders a great sense of belonging and provides for great friendships to develop.

This is what the advertisers and sponsors tap into: images of happiness, success and celebration abound; uplifting, anthemic music is added to the mix, whipping up emotions and increasing our desire to be a part of the action. There they work in the realms of human desire.

One specific TV advertising campaign comes to mind. It is promoting a particular brand of wine, Trivento. I have no idea what it tastes like, what grape it is made from, where it comes from, or anything about the product itself. And yet the advertising message is strong. The adverts typically involve a few short shots of a man going through some kind of tough but exciting physical challenge (a rugby scrum, a sky dive, abseiling down a tower, that kind of thing). This then pans out to the same man, now surrounded by his male friends, all marvelling at him telling the story of his adventure with the emphasis on the 'You should have been there.' His friends are in awe of his achievement, and all raise a glass of Trivento in celebration. In this case, not only does the wine bring them together with a common bond, but it also suggests that they become actively involved in the event itself.

Drink Trivento, and not only will you have attractive, adventurous friends, you'll become this yourself.

It's that easy.

So if Trivento gets me great friends, what of Talisker Whisky? Maybe a bit more niche, but nonetheless misleading, Talisker is a main sponsor of one of the toughest events out there. This is a rowing race across the Atlantic Ocean, which takes place every year. Not many people take up the challenge, and even fewer ever get to the starting line, let alone the finish! To embark on such a race the preparations are enormous, logistically and physically. Can you imagine the amount of training needed to get ready for this? The physical demands are simply staggering – weeks of hard rowing, day in, day out, and grabbing sleep in blocks of two hours at a time. This is not an event for the faint hearted.

And whisky is not a drink for the faint hearted! So up steps Talisker and sponsors this race. Perhaps it's the ultimate drink for the ultimate race. Only the toughest survive, or something. We all want to be a hero in some way or another, and maybe by drinking Talisker we can become part of that epic race. It's certainly not going to enhance our fitness, or help the rowers navigate through Atlantic storms with a 60-foot swell.

Football is probably the biggest game on planet Earth. It is sponsored, supported, and propped up (?) by alcohol (as well as TV rights – oh – partly paid for by the proceeds of alcohol revenues). In the UK we had the Carling Premiership, and the European 2020 Cup was sponsored by Heineken (as well as Coca-Cola). Drinking is such a part of watching sport, we now have SPORTS BARS; what a term! Drinking may no longer be allowed on the football terraces, but the pubs and clubs around the country where most of the spectators are, before, during and after the match, have free-flowing drinks.

Is it any wonder, then, with this constant barrage of drink-related images, behaviours and suggestions, that many of us find ourselves drawn in? Drink and sport are made for one another. To be part of it, partake. It's so easy.

But I wonder just how many of the best professional, and amateur, sportsmen drink to help their game.

I know that to be the best me, I'm not going to achieve it through drinking. It's an illusion. We all know it is, but we see drink and sport 'living together' so often that we barely notice it. And in the background, the insidious worm of association is at work in our brains, where it starts to make connections, to strengthen them. We are not consciously aware of or controlling this, but we are learning that drinking and doing well in sport/friendship/teams go hand in hand. In time, these links become hardwired, our modus operandi.

This is a link we need to break. We know the truth, so need to rewire our brains. Maybe we are not the sporty type, but I'm sure we all want to be a part of something, don't we? We've all got something missing from our lives, I'm sure.

Filling a hole

What is one of the simplest ways to get someone to buy your product or service? You make them believe they are missing something from their lives, and that you have the very thing they need to fill that hole. But what if there isn't anything missing? That's OK, we can make something up; the advertiser can always create something from nothing.

And so it goes. The advertiser exploits or creates a need, a desire, even a craving. He creates a hole, or finds one that nobody else has yet spotted, and suggests he has just what you need to fill it. Further, the product is generally immaterial. There's nothing fundamentally new in the world anymore; everything being a rehash of a current or past product. Instead, it's time to play on trends, emotions, to create demand from nothing or recycle old ideas into new. For the drinks' companies, this is one of the easiest things ever.

Let's just think of four things we all like and want more of, and look at how advertising gets us to buy alcohol regardless. What I'm talking about here are:

- Holidays
- Sex
- Friendship
- Escapism/excitement

That's right. Create a connection between these four and your product, and it'll fly off the shelves. For the problem drinker, the final one will resonate most since holidays become unaffordable, sex is probably off limits (or simply impossible after a few!) and friendships are strained.

For simplicity, we'll work through the list and see how we end up buying a drink after exposure to the advertising messages, starting with holidays. It's not hard to see how sun, sea and Sangria end up together. Coconuts and Malibu in the Caribbean, yes please. Cocktails such as Sex on the Beach scream holiday time, and all-inclusive deals with unlimited alcohol on tap sell like hot cakes.

But we don't even need to be so brazen about it. We see romantic couples watching a sunset from their balcony in Tuscany, clinking glasses. Even the most perfect situation can't be without alcohol. Everyone loves a good holiday, and everyone wants more of them. Creating a need is hardly difficult, and if we can bottle a holiday and sell it in the local off-licence, even better.

Alcohol is held up to be the icing on the cake of a holiday, whether it's a drunken stag on lagers, or a spa retreat with pre-dinner champagne. The message is loud and clear. Booze is part of the deal; it's just not a holiday without it. And we buy into it.

Whatever it is, holidays (taking or planning them) sell drinks.

A second pastime we all indulge in, and many want more of, is sex, and advertising a drink to appear that it'll give you sex appeal is one of the biggest sellers of all time. It doesn't even need to be product specific, although James Bond's Martini, 'Shaken, not stirred' certainly is. Watch a TV programme about couples getting together, or getting away together, and there'll be champagne thrown in. It's sexy, exclusive, seductive even. Alcohol the ice-breaker, alcohol the sophisticate. We judge people by what they drink. Picture a woman in a cocktail dress drinking a pint. Picture a man with a sherry. Picture your mate "Builder Dave" with a Pina Colada, complete with glace cherry and twirly umbrella! Maybe not! Swap them over and you get the drift. Drinks can make us appear sexier, more desirable as a partner, and so we learn that to progress in this area of our lives, drinking will enhance our chances.

Friendships are something we all enjoy, and doesn't the alcohol industry know it. You find a drinks' advert that shows a singleton drinking. I can't think of one. Somehow an advert suggesting we 'get away from it all', drinking alone in a silent flat, wouldn't work. It may be what happens, but in the mind of the drinker, watching an advert for that same drink, portraying young, healthy, happy people amongst friends is what works. Alcohol and friendship. We aspire to the second, where the hole exists (or we are told it does), and we fill that hole with alcohol. Friends drink together, alcohol provides the glue, and advertisers play on this. The thing is, even when we have drunk our friends away, we still have one; alcohol itself becomes our friend. It never lets us down. It's reliable, always available and trustworthy. Even before we get here, advertisers make alcohol seem as much of a friend as everyone else.

As well as holidays, sex and friendship, we all also love a bit of adventure in our lives. We may want to travel the world, explore what's around us, discover new experiences. I just need to turn to the Trivento adverts I mentioned earlier. I chose them because they work so well and are almost the perfect example of the genre. Featuring a group of young men, these adverts flit from scenes of scuba diving, parachuting, exciting sports, to ones of the men laughing and joking together as they recount their experiences to one another. The message? Your life lacks fun, so drink this wine and you'll have an exciting life. Yes, they are wholly unrealistic, but they appeal to our base need of belonging, friendship, fun and adventure – escapism, even.

Where we lack, so alcohol can provide. It is portrayed, and we take this in, as a solution to many of our problems in life. We need a holiday: have a drink. We need sex: have a drink. We need friends: have a drink. We need fun: have a drink. Wow, is there anything that having a drink can't do?

Just remember; these are holes created for us, by others, just so they can fill them. We may well have been conned into thinking our lives aren't up to much when in fact they are fine. Compared to fiction, they DO look less good, but that's compared to fiction. Remember that and the con isn't so clever after all; the façade is removed and we can see the truth. With the truth we can start to build our quit, separating fact from fiction. That's always a good start!

We are but cash machines

The drinks companies are there to make a profit. They are not charities, are they, unless I'm very much mistaken? They make a profit by selling to you and me, and survive and grow by selling us more, or at higher prices.

As consumers, we represent cash machines for corporations. They find the right buttons to press and we hand over cash. It's the same as us tapping in our PIN and taking money out of the ATM. There's a very simple transaction going on here. One need is satisfied (button pressed) and a reward is earned (cash given).

When it comes to pressing the buttons, akin to finding out our PIN, advertisers and marketers really do their research, working out all our wants and desires. They'll even make up new ones for us, just so they can satisfy them. And there are some universal wants out there that are so simple to see.

Take friendship. All of us appreciate it, live for it, really. We are not hermits; rather, we live in communities, constantly interacting with one another. If only an advertiser could make this interaction look happy, exciting, sexy even. Easy as pie! Put some young and attractive people together, have them laughing and smiling, clinking glasses, and there you go. Who wouldn't want a part of that? And there you have a drink commercial.

And they work. That's one PIN – friendship.

How about heroism? Picture the scene. Stormy seas, a fisherman being buffeted by waves as he hauls in his catch. His boat is being tossed in a huge swell, the navigation dials spinning like mad things. It all spells danger, risk. The next shot could be of the fisherman sitting in his local pub, beer in hand, recounting the tale of the mighty storm. 'Beer, for the brave' could be the tagline. Yes, you can tell I'm not in advertising, but you see what I mean? As a viewer, that's a strong signal to receive. Heroes drink beer. I want to be a hero. Aha, I'll drink beer. Boom! PIN accessed and out comes my wallet.

And then there's sex. Always in the top ten topics for sales. Just look at perfume. They don't advertise the actual product. They advertise its ultimate outcome. 'Wear me and you'll get some' is what they are saying, if truth be told. So we buy it, in the hope that we will suddenly become attractive and desirable. Alcohol is sold in the same way. Look, for instance, at the way in which Pimm's is advertised. Images of a specific lifestyle, one we aspire to, are projected on to our screens. We lap up the messages of 'Drink Pimm's and this is how you could live', so off we go to the supermarket and buy some!

Our desires, aspirations, and wants (known and unknown – real or not) are accessed by the drinks companies through advertising. They know what combinations of buttons to press, which emotions to target, to get us rushing out and buying their product. We may be able to keep our PIN for our bank cards to ourselves, but when it comes to our emotional PINs the advertisers know them better than we do.

They push the button, we provide the cash, and just like that the advertisers can create crazes for drinks. Many of us will remember Babycham in the 1970s. Chardonnay was all the rage in the 1980s and 1990s, and in the early 2020s, gin was in. It's almost as if these drinks become so on trend that people feel like outcasts if they aren't drinking them. It's as if fear can be used to get us buying the stuff! The manufacturers have worked hard to make them SO desirable, SO on trend and SO accessible that we simply have to be drinking them to be a part of what's going on. And we really don't like being on the outside, looking in, do we? So we buy into it, end up with umpteen different drinks at home, even post selfies with our latest on trend deliveries, special glasses and the like, and end up doing the advertising for the drinks companies ourselves! They really do know how to push our buttons, don't they?

So there you have it. We are but cash machines.

Why not keep a critical eye open when watching TV or flicking through magazines, and look more deeply at the drinks' adverts? What is the story they are telling? What are they trying to excite in your mind? What emotions are they targeting? Once you have worked it out it will be like being given the answer to a riddle. You'll never see the advert the same way again. A different light will be cast on drinking. You'll see just how much you have been influenced, some would say manipulated, into drinking.

Are you content to be manipulated? To have had your emotional PINs hijacked? Perhaps adding this to your armoury will help you in the fight to get sober, if that's what you want.

After all, the more knowledge you have, the greater your chances of success.

Promotions

Pretty much every technique is used to get us drinking. This is all layered upon the social norms of alcohol being a part of daily life, something that will, if we are to believe all we are told, actually enhance our lives. It is our susceptibility to believe all we are told, that makes these suggestions stick so easily.

Soon enough we'll come on to the fact that our brains can't tell the difference between real and imagined events, but for now just hold that thought. It is actually why such techniques as visualisation work so well. We are able to use our imagination in such a vivid way that we can do dress rehearsals in our minds, so that when it comes to the real thing, such as giving a key presentation, we are really well prepared. It's all well and good when we ourselves make use of this facility on ourselves, but we are also open to suggestion, by others who also understand how his works, and use it to their advantage when appealing to us. Some call it influence, or maybe it's manipulation.

How might it work?

Most bars these days have what they call a Happy Hour. This is a promotional period during which drinks are cheaper than usual, set at a time when the bars will usually be emptier, and aimed at bringing customers in to spend money. I've been to plenty of Happy Hours myself. I'm not sure I've ever felt a rise in mood during them, any feeling of elation and contentment as a result of drinking beer between 5:00pm and 7:00pm. Yes, that's two hours, I know, but that's generally the length of a Happy Hour, or the flat two hours they truly are.

As I said, our brains find it hard to distinguish truth from fiction. It will read that there is a Happy Hour and immediately clicks into the thought that this is a good idea. 'Happy' sounds positive, and we like positive experiences. After all, it is a deep-rooted instinct to make sure we keep ourselves content, as well as safe and secure, and the concept of Happy Hour fulfils this. The very fact that it is two hours is relevant only in so much as it gives us a further pleasant surprise – double happiness!

Happy Hour is a vehicle to shift beer, not to make us happy. It plays on our basic human needs and provides a route to satisfy them. As our brains start to get excited about being happy, we go along with the illusion.

A second promotional technique that is often used is that of giving away a free sample. We all love something for nothing, a bargain, and nothing shouts louder than free. It provides effortless satisfaction. It also sets off a feedback loop in our brains, one that requires us to reciprocate. At some point, having been through the 'take, take, take' cycle, it's time for us to give. And by give, I mean buy. At that point – bingo! – The promotion has worked, for the promoter. We are now a customer, not just a prospect, and the chances are we will buy more both now and in the future. As they say, there's no such thing as a free lunch!

I remember one such promotion being held when I was at university. It was summertime, early June, I recall. We were enjoying those long warm evenings we all dream about, and it was summer party season. In the corner of the quad, a beer company had set up a stall, a miniature bar. It was the shape of a beer can, and manned by two beautiful people, of course. There was a hall party going on this particular night, and it was being sponsored by a well-known brand of American beer. The usual hall bar was also open, as well as this free bar.

Until such time as they had run out of stock, the free bar simply handed out bottles of chilled beer to students. What wasn't to like? Every student loves a drink. Every student is skint! I was in my element, but also doing what so many people do when there is a free bar, drinking far more than usual – because it's free!

It's almost like our degree of thirst rises as the price falls. And when it's free? We are insatiable!

Half-price drinks in Happy Hour will get us drinking when we normally wouldn't. Free samples get us drinking more than usual because it's free. Just look at free bars at office parties or weddings. People simply take advantage and hit the booze that much harder. Which brings me on to two clear observations; one about promotions themselves, and another about the hold alcohol has on society.

First, a quick one. Beer companies do not give drinks away unless it's worthwhile. They understand that a large enough number of those who have had the free drinks will come back in the future and buy their brand again and again. Whether it be loyalty, reciprocation or whatever, the drinks companies know that giving away free drinks is, in the long run, a profitable activity.

Second, what does the behaviour of many tell us about our drinking habits? Presented with a choice of a drink that costs money or one that is free, which would you take? If one was gin and the other beer, the choice might be simple; you'd take the one you liked. If, however, there were two different wines, one being your usual drink (which you would pay for) and the other one that you had not yet come across or tried before (which would be free), then the choice would be more difficult. I would suggest that it, being free, would cause you to pick the new one. This would be more likely if you'd already had a drink or two. Further into the evening, pretty much anything would do, as long it was alcohol, even if you'd never normally drink it.

But if we had to pay? We'd drink far less, and we'd be far choosier about what we drank. Perhaps the amount we drink is really down to cost, then. Maybe, as free bars tend to produce more drunkenness that pay bars! Thus, given free rein, maybe more of us than we think are unable to control our intake, find it hard to flick the off switch when our wallets or purses usually do that for us.

If you think you may be a problem drinker, then you are probably less alone than you think you are. A drinks promotion may illustrate that very well indeed. These promotions prey on our desire to be happy. Happy Hour is a blatant and successful call to action; a free bar appeals to our sense of getting a bargain, some kind of instant gratification.

Maybe they show our drinking habits for what they really are or would turn into, given half a chance. Maybe promotions shine a light on a bigger problem in society, a greater level of addiction than we see on the surface.

Have a think about how promotions make you feel, what thoughts come to mind when you come across them. What are the promoters trying to make you FEEL, and then DO? Considering and understanding this may help us defend ourselves from their intentions for us to buy more – and thereby consume more – alcohol.

Soaps and dramas

In your fight against drinking alcohol, one of the main lessons you'll need to learn, or at least need to become aware of, is just how much we are being programmed to accept and expect it as part of our daily lives. Nowhere is this more clearly seen than in TV and film.

In these mediums, we are subjected, almost constantly, to the process of normalising the consumption of alcohol. This is done to such an extent that alcohol becomes, absolutely, an essential part of life. What we are looking at is the all-pervading, insidious role alcohol plays across drama, soap opera and, in particular, crime shows.

Let's pick just three shows here. This does not mean they are any better or worse than any others, it's just that I'm sure everyone, at least in Britain, will have come across them at some point. The other key factor about these is that they have longevity, are well written and generally superbly acted. Like them or not, they are of the highest quality and realism.

First up we have *Peaky Blinders*. Set in the Birmingham underworld of racing and gambling in the early part of the 20th century, the darker sides of life are glamorised, and we all start to love the main protagonist: a violent, ruthless, and broken man, but also something of a charmer. It is almost as if whenever there is a real problem to deal with, when something has gone badly wrong, when someone is hurt, or gets married, or brokers a brilliant deal, or has one over an enemy, drink is brought out. Whisky will sort out all ills, will enhance all successes and will erase all failures. At least that's how it seems to work in *Peaky Blinders*.

Not only that, but drinking also seems to enable the characters to make better decisions. (Why else would they drink?) Occasionally, exceptionally, the drink will take them over the edge, but this is rare. Nobody really suffers from hangovers; drink is their friend. From dingy pubs and hip flasks to glamourous flapper girl cocktails and even the mafia, alcohol is omnipresent. One character has a drink problem in this show. It is portrayed brilliantly, and with sympathy, but his ways are so detached from ours that making connections, empathising, is hard. Instead, we are drawn to feel pity.

Watching this show, of which I am a great fan, I understand that drinking was very much a part of what went on then. It is used to great dramatic effect; it is normal and a part of the life of these characters whom we buy into, generally connect with and become involved with. Combine this with what we know about how the brain works (i.e. not recognising fact from fiction) and how it then creates and emphasises what it perceives, and we grow more and more into the impression that alcohol is normal, acceptable and even useful in our lives. This is what our brains have learned, by seeing it every day, and without understanding that, it is very difficult to change.

It is the process of becoming aware of this that starts the re-education process, a process that takes time and patience, but is, ultimately, simple as it is merely a matter of opening our eyes to a new perspective on life.

The second example is of two great British soaps, *EastEnders* and *Coronation Street*. Unlike *Peaky Blinders*, these are set in the present day, and this brings total realism to them. We see actors playing out storylines that are actually in the news and current affairs are portrayed.

They are about as real as you can get. Yet they are total fiction, stories made up for our entertainment. The other nod to realism is that, central to both, is a pub. *EastEnders* has the Queen Vic and it's the Rover's Return for *Coronation Street*, and much of the action revolves around these pubs. Many of the most dramatic scenes take place in, around or as a result of something happening in the pub.

The two pubs are the centre of their respective communities. It's almost that they hold everything together. And as viewers, we watch people drinking, getting on with their lives (for better or for worse), in these pubs. This is the way things are, and through these scenes, we are further immersed in the world of consuming alcohol, even if we aren't drinking ourselves.

Watch a soap opera. It will have a pub or bar, and it's around that which much of the action revolves. What this tells our brains is that pubs and bars are a normal - even necessary - part of our lives. Mix in the fantastic acting and realism of a show designed to reflect our own lives, and differentiating between fact and fiction becomes almost impossible.

Finally, I'd like to present *Life on Mars* and *Ashes to Ashes*, crime dramas of the highest order yet again. Slightly quirky and unusual, we step back in time to an age when political correctness and equal rights had barely been conceived. Smoky offices and whisky bottles in desk drawers, these were unusual times. I even remember watching chat shows from this era where guests and even presenters would be smoking, and drinking, on live TV. It might seem bizarre now, but that's just how it was in those days. I was a pre-teen myself then, and watched it all unfold in front of my very eyes as I grew up. Perhaps that's why I love these two shows so much - a bit of nostalgia, even though they were far from 'good' old days.

These are accessible and fun, gritty and engaging, shows. Alcohol plays a big part in them, from police officers drinking in pubs after a long shift, to their drinking late into the night in the station. Helping to numb the pain of failure, out comes the whisky, or to celebrate a success, alcohol does its job in these shows as it did back then! We are so easily sucked into these worlds of make-believe that our neural pathways, already laid out to see that alcohol is a great companion in good times and bad, are simply strengthened. More and more we understand that alcohol provides the answer. We believe this because wherever we turn, we see that being portrayed. It becomes the norm.

Being able to break out of this, to set up new pathways, by thinking critically and actively about what we see, is an enormous step in our journey towards quitting. By opening our eyes to the truth, and resetting our accepted views of the world, we can start to move away from alcohol as being central to our being. To do this, we need to change the filter through which we see the world and perceive reality. It's as easy as changing a filter on your camera; we just need to make a conscious effort to do it and, over time, we will begin to see the world in a new, and alcohol-free way. We will see it for what it is, and be able to make better choices about our consumption.

Bottles and glasses

When we boil it down to its bare essentials, and contemplating what we have just learned, we know alcohol is a dangerous poison. We mix it with other ingredients to make it palatable. It remains a poison. It is also a mind-altering substance. When we consume it, our state of mind changes. We may become giggly, emotional or aggressive. Whatever happens, when we consume alcohol we become a slightly or significantly different person.

So, given that we know alcohol is a poison that alters our very core and eventually will do for us, how is it that an intelligent, thinking, rational being like us will drink it? Consider my cat. If I were to waft a glass of red wine under his nose, his face would wrinkle and he would probably run away. Stanley knows what's good for him, and avoids what isn't. He'll avoid alcohol. He instinctively knows that it's bad for him. He doesn't need studies and surveys, experiments and doctors. He just knows. Much as I love Stanley, he can't tell me why alcohol is bad, but by simply watching him, I can tell he's never going near the stuff.

So how is it that a supposedly more developed creature, that has moved to the top of the animal kingdom, consumes the stuff? Avoiding poison and danger and risk are what keeps animals alive. But humans seem to invite it in, and many will suffer and die as a result.

Let's not concern ourselves with that just yet. Let's just say our arrogance leads us all to believe; 'It'll never happen to me.'

Instead, let's accept our own position as an animal, one that has, over the centuries, embraced alcohol, absorbed into our culture right across the globe and in almost every society. There are a few exceptions, but generally speaking, alcohol has always been and remains central to human culture. Alcohol has even worked its way into spiritual and religious customs. Christians drink wine as 'the blood of Christ' during Communion, for example.

Our customs have developed over time. Producers of alcoholic drinks have, similarly, developed over time. Drinking habits have also changed over the years, and it may well be that today, for the first time, we are actually seeing our younger generation turning away from alcohol. Initial indications are showing that. Whether this is a blip or a long-term trend, only time will tell.

However, while drinkers remain, it seems that everyone is vying for a piece of the action, or at least the pound in our pocket. We, as a species, have elevated alcohol to a new level, worship it almost. This is abundantly clear when we look at how we consume it.

We pour it out of bottles, into glasses, whilst sitting in bars surrounded by music and conversation, art and architecture. Yes, we also drink straight from the can on our sofa, but let's park that thought for now, and return to the bottle, the glass and the bar.

Perhaps the most common of containers, the bottle is a ubiquitous article. Made of glass, it doesn't leak or taint its content with any colour or flavour. It's perfect for the job it does. But that's not all. Bottles are made in specific shapes, sizes, colours and designs to indicate what's in them. Baileys, Gordon's gin, Malibu, Paul Masson carafe, Coca-Cola: all immediately recognisable, memorable, and useful at the same time.

And that's just the start of it. It's almost as if the bottle has become as important as the contents. Exquisite designs abound. These bottles are like works of art themselves, collector's items almost. And that's the point. Designed to grab our attention, the bottle sells the product. The contents are very much the same. Rhubarb gin is rhubarb gin is rhubarb gin. Put it in a rhubarb-shaped bottle and wham! That's the one to buy!

The same is true for all drinks; the bottle sells it. Vodka bottles are now becoming more and more extravagant as well. Although I can't stand the stuff, I absolutely love some of the designs. They really are quite stunning. The bottle has stepped up and into the world of sculpture, and it's doing rather well there, too! Looking at these bottles on the shelves I can see exactly how they work.

If I buy the stylish bottle, I am a stylish person.

One drink has gone to the extreme, and I'm not sure how it works. Absinthe is often contained in skull-shaped bottles. I'll leave that one there. You can ponder it for yourself!

Once we have purchased the bottle, or chosen which drink we will be having, then comes the glass. Will it be a schooner (sherry) or a tankard (beer)? Perhaps a flute (champagne) or a Martini glass (cocktails)? On and on the list goes. There's a different glass for almost every drink. A bowl for warming brandy, a squat piece of cut glass for whisky. This then gets down to the personal level. In my old village pub, drinkers would even have their own glasses. They'd insist their beer tasted better out of them. I won't argue.

The point is that we have taken alcohol to such a level that we honour it with its own glass from which to drink it.

We don't sup wine from a mug, or beer from the stirrup cup. Custom, tradition, culture and alcohol, intertwined and virtually inseparable; this is the world many of us are brought up in and in which we live our lives.

Where we drink is now undergoing something of a revolution. It is becoming a critical part of so many people's identity. Just look at the change over the past 30 years. The old-style village pubs serving beer and maybe some nuts (certainly no meals) are dying. High-design, high-style, high-chic bars are on the rise. Where you drink seems to be much more important than anything else. Nowadays, in our society where instant gratification is king, celebrity is worshipped, and style wins out against substance, being seen in the right places is simply crucial.

OK, maybe I have gone over the top but the point is that more and more we are focusing on all that *surrounds* the drink, rather than the drink, which itself remains a poison. It will still make you drunk, wherever or whoever you are. It will still cause regret, embarrassment and more.

Petrol will burn when you put a match to it. Likewise, alcohol will change you, wherever you drink it. The difference is that we don't always know what we'll change into.

But drinking is still a fantastically glamourous thing to do, right? If alcohol is such a great thing, and it's fashionable to be seen drinking the right drinks, with the right people, in the right bars and clubs, what happens when it all gets too much, when we start finding that we're having a drink when we never did before? When the glitz starts wearing thin, what happens?

Maybe we need to be a little more careful, keep some things to ourselves. Once we realise that alcohol has lied to us and has ensnared us, it's very hard to live an honest and open life. So, we start lying to ourselves, and that's when we know we are in trouble.

It is now that alcohol starts taking away more than it gives us, but we will not notice the point at which this happened, for we will have lied our way through it.

WE ALL FALL DOWN

The cycle of addiction

An addiction to any substance will provide a considerable number of highs, actual and perceived. After all, without the highs, there wouldn't be an addiction. As people we also want to feel on top of the world. A high gives us that feeling.

But after a high, there comes a low. To get out of the low, we seek the next high, and on it goes.

Down we go.

When we first take a drink, and for many of our early drinks, we feel very different from normal. We get a giddy feeling, a light-headedness, and we may feel somewhat detached from the world. Many of us like this. These feelings are often accompanied by good things happening, being with friends, at a party, a celebration and so on.

Over time, our unconscious mind associates drinking alcohol with having a good time. (By the way, we would have had a good time anyway, but our mind can't know that.) Each time we take a drink thereafter, our mind thinks, *Yay, good time coming. Let's have another drink.* In fact, the power of our mind is such that it will kick off these euphoric feelings we get from drinking alcohol BEFORE we have had even a sip. Our mind anticipates the perceived pleasure and brings it to life.

Over the years, as we gradually build up a tolerance to alcohol; it will take more and more to get the feeling we once had from just a single glass. Our mind will still associate drinking alcohol with providing a benefit, with a good time. However, what was initially a benefit of having a great time eventually turns on us. For if alcohol makes a good time better, or lifts our mood, then it follows that it would make a bad time, less bad, or better, even. Even more so, if one drink makes us feel good, two must make us feel twice as good, and so on. Once we have made those connections, which are not such great leaps, we will very quickly turn to drink to make us feel up when we are down, or better when we are up. The problem is that this only works for a short while, and soon enough we never feel as good as we used to before we started drinking, even when we believe we are better off than we were.

This is because, as the weeks and months pass, the ups that drinking alcohol gives us when we are naturally happy become less up. Further, as we progress in our drinking, we also tend to use it more and more to remedy the downs, rather than enhance the ups. Sadly, alcohol's ability to boost the downs into ups lessens over time. This is simply how it works. If alcohol always made good times even better than the last good time, and changed all our bad times into happy ones, everyone would be drinking all the time! And we all know that doesn't happen.

Let's now look at how the descent actually works, with the help of our imagination. We all have a natural state of being, a reasonable level of contentment. Let us imagine a straight, horizontal line across a page, with time moving left to right. There is also a wavy line on the page, and this is our 'how we feel when we drink alcohol' line. Imagine that this line moves up and down, in waves (peaks and troughs) over time. The peaks are when we have just had a drink. The troughs are when we have not. Our mind controls this line. It has associated a drink with a good time, so the line goes up when we drink. By the same logic, the line goes down when we have not had a drink, and we have that 'I need a drink' niggle (which turns into an uncontrollable urge the deeper we get into alcohol dependency). By drinking, we ensure that the wavy line always peaks above the horizontal "I feel normal" line in the early days, towards the left. This is where we learn that alcohol 'is' a pleasure enhancer. You will also see that after each peak there is a trough, and this is always below the normal line, so we always feel worse than normal after a drink. (Let's call it a hangover!) Our mind also knows it can feel better if it has a drink. So we drink again and guess what? We are above the normal line – happier than we are in our usual state of stable contentment. For a while, the dips are a price worth paying for the good times.

At some point – and this will be different for all of us – the peaks in the wavy 'with alcohol' line will not quite reach the level of normal contentment. We will be permanently less content than we were before we started drinking. We also now believe that the only way to feel better is to drink, and now the lows are lower and the highs never high enough. Yet we still chase them. We now drink even more in our attempts to feel normal again but each drink takes us further and further away from that. This is why dependent drinkers drink more and more over time.

Where do you think you sit on this line? What does it tell you about your drinking?

The downward cycle of addiction is a self-fuelling cycle. It only ever accelerates in that direction. The only way out is to break the cycle, to re-educate our unconscious mind. As long as that mind sees benefit in drinking alcohol, it will ensure we drink alcohol.

By removing alcohol, we remove the need for alcohol.

Almost immediately we stop drinking, the wavy line will start edging back up towards the 'feeling normal' horizontal, and lose its extreme highs and lows. We will

117

stop experiencing such big peaks and troughs, and life will become more stable. There will always be ups and downs, that's part and parcel of life itself, but without alcohol they will be much less extreme, and so we'll be able to manage them without fuss. These waves will subside from being a massive storm into a gentle swell, and be much easier to ride.

This is a really positive message. So often we talk about a vicious cycle, of spiralling out of control and so on. But there is another way to look at this, to look at the virtuous cycle.

Riding the thermals

Traditionally, we only imagine a behavioural spiral as a negative, an almost inevitable and self-fulfilling decline. The spiralling of water down the plughole is clearly visible, as we watch the water drain away, to be gone.

But I'd like to think of a different spiral, one we can use to work our minds in a positive way. That spiral is one we see in eagles, riding the thermals, rising ever higher as they circle above. They gain height so they can move on from one place to another, gliding vast distances between, before finding a new thermal upon which to rise again.

Each time they rise, these birds soar higher, glide further, see more and more of the ground below them, gaining a broader perspective of the world.

This is how I see myself changing the further I get from my last drink. I feel I am rising above temptation, and as I glide from one day or week to the next, I am able to use those days without a drink as if they were thermals. I am not saying that every day or week is perfect. From time to time there is stillness, no wind, no thermals, and I can find myself going nowhere, achieving little. That is fine, and I am happy that not all days are amazing, exciting and full of achievements. Some are just generally OK, some downright dull, some disastrous. That's the way of things.

Good days happen. Bad days happen. It's how we react to them that matters. As I move away from my drinking days, I am better able to cope with the bad days and turn them into average or OK days, and good days into great days. When drinking, a bad day was an out-and-out disaster, only to be washed away with alcohol. A good day could never become great with alcohol, but it could easily turn bad. We've seen that a couple of times already, and I'm sure you can think of some such days from your own experiences, or recall a friend who's been there.

The downward spiral was always waiting for me when I was drinking. Now that I am sober, I am able to catch the thermals and enjoy the view. Problems shrink as I rise above them, and the big picture emerges, a vast landscape of possibilities below.

As each sober day passes, the risk of being caught in the downward spiral reduces. It may never go away, I must remember that, but I don't want to leave the view from where I am.

Yes, there is a cycle of addiction. Maybe there's also a cycle of recovery. I like to think so.

Before we can start on that path, we need to have reached a point so low that, quite simply, the only way is up. How low that is will be different for each and every one of us, and there is no race to the bottom or kudos in having been lower than the next person. We all have our own, and we'll know what it is.

Emotions

Central to our very being, our emotions drive almost every aspect of our behaviour. It is no different when it comes to addiction, and so an understanding of our emotions is a fantastic way of coming to terms with the road ahead.

Let's make a start, and dive right in:

The Big Six

The six, as provided by verywellmind.com*, are as follows:

1. Happiness
2. Sadness
3. Fear
4. Disgust
5. Anger
6. Surprise

As a drinker, we can find a great reason or justification to drink alongside every emotion. I know I did, so let's have a look at me, as it's who I know best. I also reckon I'm pretty representative of problem drinkers, having been one for over 20 years. I'm sure you'll get some 'that sounds familiar' moments or 'been there, done that' memories flashing up!

So, let's now dive into some examples of how we drink on our emotions, and what that might mean.

* www.verywellmind.com/an-overview-of-the-types-of-emotions-4163976

1. Happiness

Perhaps the happiest days we have are wedding days. They are also full of alcohol and drunken uncles. They are the scenes of regrettable behaviour and of high emotion. The day is all about bringing two people who love each other together. It is a celebration of that love. We toast the Bride and Groom, the Happy Couple. Nothing should be needed to make anyone happier; how could such a mood be improved upon? But we have free bars, and endless drinks that we start guzzling before lunch on empty stomachs. Drunk beyond memory at my nephew's wedding a couple of years ago, I have no recollection of most of the day and evening. I know I started feeling great, it was a glorious day, but as soon as that fist sip went down I was a write-off.

Think of any happy occasion, and we tend to throw in alcohol. Birthdays, births, passing exams and going on holiday all involve drinking these days. Look at an airport lounge at 4:30am and you'll see people with pints of lager. At 4:30am, for crying out loud! And these are not your street drinkers. No, these are your mums and dads heading off for a week on the Costa del Sol. Alcohol really does do funny things to normal folk in happy times!

2. Sadness

Ever wanted to 'drown your sorrows', but never quite found the answer at the bottom of the glass? If things weren't going as planned, which was quite regularly, I'd have a drink to help me forget about it all. Getting into a state of inebriation would deaden me to any sadness. I drank at my nephew's wedding and I drank at my mother's funeral. I got in a state at both. There was nothing different in the alcohol; it didn't change at all. My emotions were different and yet I added alcohol to both, to enhance my happiness and deaden the pain of my sadness. What a wonderous substance this alcohol is to be able to do both. But no, all it did was flatten me, remove my ability to recall the day, slow me, make me incoherent and, at the end of each event, render me unconscious, passing out in bed without knowing how I got there.

3. Fear

Have you ever used alcohol to pluck up a bit of Dutch courage? When faced with an unusual or unfamiliar situation, all of us experience a certain amount of fear. A natural reaction that puts us on high alert. This is an instinct that served us well in our more ancient past when we were cavemen and in danger from wild beasts, but at a party? Fear still kicks in. I recall being petrified (i.e. stuck to the spot) with fear at teenage parties, when everyone else was getting up and asking girls to dance. I simply couldn't do it. I was painfully shy, so scared it seems feeble. The answer was to kill the fear, send it packing, and this was done by drinking it away, by giving myself some Dutch courage.

The only problem was that by the time I had plucked up enough courage I couldn't string a sentence together. I'd rendered myself incapable and certainly most unattractive to anyone, so I'd sit back down and say to myself, 'It'll be better next time.' It never was. I'd get the fear, drink and cycle round the same old rubbish. Same action, same outcome – surprise, surprise!

4. Disgust

For me, I'd put drinking on disgust into the self-pity category. I was certainly in the 'poor me' camp. The disgust usually came after a bout of drinking had left me in bad way, and I'd be suffering the day after. Given the chance, I'd be back in the pub as soon as it opened. (How many times did I walk around finding the one that opened first – and why did I not know which it was?) I would order a beer and go and sit in the quietest corner, away from everybody else, nursing the glass with my head bowed down. I'd simply sit and think, over and over again: *How did it come to this? How can I be here? What has gone wrong?* I'd be appalled with myself, and yet I'd be drinking at the same time. It was all I knew to take the shame away. I was asking, asking, asking questions of myself. I never found an answer. Not in that first pint, nor in any of those that followed. It wasn't until I put the drink down that the disgust went away, the follow-up drink went away, and I didn't need to ask questions or seek answers anymore. The subject matter was no longer there; my disgust in myself was gone. The reason for this behaviour was gone, so the behaviour, too, was gone.

5. Anger

Perhaps the most powerful, certainly the most destructive, of my emotions, is that I can get angry about pretty much anything. From the state of world politics to a sweet wrapper on the pavement, I'll get angry. I'll get angry with other people for behaving in certain ways, then do the same myself and think nothing of it. Wound up with anger, I'd use a drink to calm down. It's not just me. You look at the TV or read a book: they are strewn with instances when a friend puts a drink in front of someone with a, 'Come on, this will calm you down.' Just look at *Peaky Blinders*, one of the best TV shows of all time. A rush of anger, and out comes the whisky. It's as if it will douse the flames of ire. Whilst many people will have a nice cup of tea, it doesn't cut it like a whisky, does it?

Drinking to quell our anger, we also face the prospect of drinking increasing our anger. Booze sends some people into a giggly state, others go quiet, but some get angry, violent. What a drug: it will both calm and provoke, and we don't really know which until it's too late. Take a look at a hospital waiting room late on Saturday night and you'll see what anger plus drink or drink plus anger can do. It's a very dangerous combination indeed.

6. *Surprise*

A surprise party, a surprise gift, any surprise will knock us a little off balance. We can also get nasty surprises, and these give us a feeling of unease. Either way, what the emotion of surprise will do is remove ourselves from our natural state, our equilibrium. We will feel little off balance. I'm sure this has happened to you as well?

Throughout pre-history we developed to be on the lookout for danger, for the unknown, as this always had the potential to do us harm. Today we remain suspicious of anything and anyone we do not know. We talk of things such as 'stranger danger', and we do what we can to protect ourselves, especially from nasty surprises.

And if one does come about, we so often hear something along the lines of, 'Here, have a drink. It'll settle you down. It'll calm your nerves.' OK, alcohol does dull the senses, slow our reactions and send us slowly towards a stupor. But is that really sensible when you've just encountered something that has the potential to harm, emotionally or physically? Aren't we better off staying totally alert, keeping away from rather than consuming alcohol?

Surprise puts us on alert, heightens our senses and keeps us safe. Knocking this flat with a drink seems about as sensible as removing the brakes from our car.

Other emotions

Look up on any site or in any book and you'll find many, many more emotions, subsets of emotions and so on. Do this now and then have a good think about a time when you have experienced each or any of those emotions. Maybe you accompanied them with a drink, or can picture a drink alongside them at some point in the future. We drinkers are exceptionally good at manipulating situations and emotions as reasons or excuses to have a drink. But do those drinks really help or merely stifle any emotion, dulling everything from fear to excitement into a more generally lethargic state?

Sober, we get to experience all our emotions in full technicolour. Life really does take on a new dimension, and we are fully there we cope with whatever comes along so much more easily.

Humans are emotional beings, so let's be fully human. And perhaps we can use our emotions to our advantage when approaching our quit.

But first, a bit more about fear because, when considering quitting drinking alcohol, perhaps the most common emotion is fear:

- Fear of failure.
- Fear of success.

126

- Fear of change.
- Fear of action.
- Fear of inaction.

As Susan Jeffers puts it so well in her book *Feel the Fear and Do It Anyway*, it all comes down to one simple fear: the fear of

'I can't handle it'.

What is it about fear, then, that keeps us rooted to the spot?

Standing out, letting people down, making a fool of ourselves, breaking promises, 'you are not worthy' judgement, we are filled with negativity from early in our lives. We start life full of promise, hope and vision. We have ambitions to fly to the moon. Slowly these dreams are taken away from us as we are told to curb our wild ambitions and be realistic. We are forced into a social norm, and breaking out of this fills us all with fear.

All of us have this fear, and we must face it or wither and die.

Many people will drink out of fear. We are afraid of the world and never feel as if we fit in. We fear being left behind in some way, and we fear being alone. To keep this fear at bay, I know I drank. It gave me an identity, a community. It also gave me some element of confidence I guess, but even then, by the time I'd quashed my fear I was too drunk to be of any use to anyone so, fearful of making a fool of myself, I found comfort in my glass. Next time would be better, I'd tell myself, next time. Next time never did work out when I drank. It was only when I quit that things started looking up.

But the fear was still there, like a constant companion. It had this enormous hold on me. It kept me drinking, but did me no favours, and it held me back from quitting because I didn't know what not drinking would be like, and that was scary in its own right. A life without booze? Seriously?

When we are faced with a scary or dangerous situation, we use our 'fight of flight' instinct, which we are all familiar with. We take on our enemy (whatever that is) or scarper to safety, well away from it. There is also a third way: we freeze. In this state we are literally stuck to the spot, unable to move. We are, in essence, paralysed. We can't move anywhere, can't fight and can't run away. Frozen, we stay exactly where we are.

This is the state many drinkers find themselves in when it comes to quitting, and I know that I was one myself. I found myself fearing drinking for the rest of my life and I found myself fearing not drinking ever again.

My fear was based on what? It came from my imagination and fed on itself.

My fear was based on the massive assumption that the rest of the world actually gives a shit!

Does Mike over the road actually care if I drink or not? NO! Does the barman think I'm some kind of loser if I order a cola? NO! Does the waiter ask me to leave a restaurant when I ask for iced water rather than wine with my meal? NO! Nobody actually cares – not at all, not one little bit – when you don't drink alcohol. They care more when you do, then vomit on their carpet! But that's not a good kind of care, is it?

128

Indeed, if someone does care that you don't drink, they are either an ally or an enemy. An ally will not judge but respect you. This is a friend. Your enemy will question, maybe ridicule you, try to get you to have a drink. Move away; they are not your friend.

When you take away the foundation upon which your fear is based – that the world gives a shit – then your fear has nowhere to base itself, and it will fade away. Believe me, your fear will be replaced by fearlessness, a feeling of strength and invincibility when you quit, and the longer you have quit for, the stronger it will be.

Do not fear situations that don't exist (i.e. the future) or people that don't matter. Don't think you are so important that the rest of the world cares. You are not the centre of the universe, and your quit is for you and not them. Remember that and because the quit is yours and yours alone, a few bumps and stumbles along the way will not faze you.

Control, or go with the flow?

As we have all probably heard, there is no good or bad, there just *is*. It is our reaction to any given situation that pigeonholes it as good or bad. A win for the Reds is bad if you are a Blues fan, but good if you follow Reds. To an impartial observer, the result just *is*.

Emotionally, the impartial observer will not react, but a Red or Blue fan would feel passion, heartbreak, elation, frustration and so on. Once we get more and more involved and interested in something we start to care deeply. The highs and lows of being a sports fan are what makes it exciting, and there's always the next game when it will come good!

Being a sports fan has one major drawback though, and that is that the average fan has absolutely no control over what happens in the game. That is down to the coaches, players, conditions, opposition – referee, even. As a fan I can shout and scream and jump up and down, but it's not going to change things. A home crowd does play a part, but that's a crowd, not me. However involved I feel during a game, I have no influence over it, I can't change it, and yet I still get worked up about it. The game itself just *is*; it's my view that gives it meaning, that makes the result good or bad.

What we also know, and will have experienced throughout our drinking careers, is that we tend to drink more when we feel bad, or even good. I know I did. These were the times I would head off alone and get drunk so I could forget all the shit in my life, and escape from it all. I could be alone in my own house, in the pub, in the park, but with drink inside of me I was doing all I could to get away from the bad situation. At other times I was in a great mood, and drinking to excess would come easily. It was as if a valve had been released.

The question now comes down to what is a bad or a good situation, and how drinking has anything to do with my fictional Reds and Blues. For me and I'm sure for many others, drinking goes hand in hand with success and failure. We 'raise a glass' and 'toast' success, or we 'drown our sorrows'.

There's a drink for every emotion, a drink for every occasion. For each and every occasion, we all judge them good or bad in varying degrees. A wedding is good, a funeral bad. Just about everything we do brings one of these opposing views and we react accordingly. We are emotional beings and our emotions drive our behaviour. Our emotions are built on our take on a situation, on our reaction to it.

Here's a list of some emotions you will all be familiar with. Have a look at them and think how each one will lead to a drink, based on your own personal experience:

- Suffering
- Excitement
- Anxiety
- Grief
- Despair
- Joy
- Sulkiness
- Awe
- Admiration
- Hatred
- Anger

- Love
- Guilt
- Pride
- Pity
- Helplessness
- Fear
- Shame

Think what this tells you before moving on. Reflect on this, take your time. You may want to go for a walk to mull this over, before carrying on here.

So, welcome back! All I know is that I used to be able to find a reason to drink, come what may. There was always at least one emotion going on inside of me, and that was all I needed. I'd use that emotion as a reason to drink. I embraced it and went with it. I spent my life going with the flow, because in that flow I could always drink. Life was one situation after another. An event would unfold, an emotion would follow and I would act, by drinking on that emotion. I was that simple. I did not question it. Actually, I put no effort into it. I was allowing life to happen around me. Not only was I going with the flow, but I was also a shipwreck being tossed on an angry ocean, and not even attempting to get back to harbour. I didn't even contemplate there being one.

So, what to do?

Fortunately that's actually really simple and practical. It is something we can all do, takes very little effort, and will yield great results. It's called a pause.

Typically, this is what will happen:

In any given Situation > we will have a Reaction > which will provoke an Emotion > and we will take an Action (drink).

We have been doing this without thinking for years and years, and we don't even notice it. Indeed, we move through the steps so quickly that all we see and experience is Situation →Drink. If we want to quit drinking, all we need to do is press pause for a few seconds from time to time. Let's consider getting home from work after a tough day, and run through the four-point sequence:

- Situation = End of a tough day.
- Reaction = Thank goodness that's over.
- Emotion = Relaxation.
- Action = Drink.

Or after an argument

- Situation = Argument.
- Reaction = I need out.
- Emotion = Anger.
- Action = Drink.

So where do we hit pause, and what does that do? Where we hit pause isn't all that important, as long as it's before the 'Action' phase. Take a few seconds between Situation and Reaction, take a deep breath and consider where you may be headed. Do the same between Reaction and Emotion, especially if you haven't managed to before. Try not to let an emotion form automatically; consider it for a moment.

All we are doing here is taking a matter of seconds, thinking *Is this for the best?* during that pause, then moving on. Stepping out, being an impartial observer rather than an involved fan, will help change your emotional state and help you keep away from the final step – 'Action' (drink).

It may not work every time, but it will get easier and easier the more you practise, and it takes so little effort, just remembering to do it, and simply deliberating for a couple of seconds of your day. I trust that you are willing to give up a couple of seconds to stay sober?

After all, the more of your life you live sober, the more joy you get from it.

Pleasure centres

Human beings seek pleasure because, by and large, the things that bring us pleasure are those that increase our chances of survival. If our ancestors hadn't craved food and sex, for example, they wouldn't have lived very long or had many offspring. To some extent, all of us are, as Freud put it, driven by the 'pleasure principle'.

What's interesting here is that as we have moved from being primitive cave-dwellers to living in modern apartments our cravings have moved on. No longer do we have survival issues, on the whole, with sourcing food or evading predators, and so our urges need satisfying in other ways. Maybe it's this that drives us to be thrill-seekers, to ride rollercoasters or to watch horror films. There is a rush of adrenalin and excitement in all of these and, as humans, we are drawn to this.

Our drive to consume sugar is based on ancient needs, but now that we have it in abundance we overconsume. We still adore sweetness, crave it, and find it incredibly hard to resist. Do you? In our distant past this made sense. Today it doesn't, but the desire remains.

The pleasure centres of the brain, ancient and powerful, drive us and all animals. Given a straightforward choice between chemically induced bliss and food, experiments have shown that rats will head for bliss, overriding the need for food, and will die as a result, as shown by Charles Duhigg in his book "The Power of Habit".

These are strong, primal urges, and our brains are not just born with them, they learn them too. I also know this from experience. Drunk, I will choose more drink over food.

Hungover? Hair of the dog! Feeling low? A pick-me-up (drink).

With our ancient brains seeking pleasure, existing in the stresses and constraints of a modern society, we head for the nearest thing that will satisfy. It could be drugs, or sex, or, most commonly and most easily accessible and acceptable, alcohol. For many, alcohol becomes the go-to feel-good hit. Our brains soon demand it, and once they learn a way of tickling our pleasure centres they won't stop demanding! And the more we provide that pleasure, the more it is demanded.

We soon develop a habit, but one that involves an addictive chemical. We then, quite unknowingly, become addicted. By the time we realise this has happened, we are well and truly stuck, and need to find our way out. Unless we do, we will continue the cycle of craving and drinking, craving and drinking. The problem is that over time we need to consume more and more to get the same effect, and in so doing feel worse and worse. To make ourselves feel better, our pleasure centres demand more alcohol, as they 'know' this makes us feel better (and, in the end, only slightly less bad than before). Eventually, no matter how much we drink, we still feel bad.

To overcome this addictive habit, we should look to install a new and healthier one. We will be venturing into new territory here and that can make us nervous, even fearful. We have already seen what fear can do to us, often keeping us rooted to the spot. But if we make a move, what is the worst thing that could possibly happen? If we make some kind of an attempt to move away from alcohol, we may not succeed. That's it! It's not like we'll lose an arm or leg and so have good reason to be frightened. All that might

136

happen is we don't quit right away. Big deal. We can try again another time. As we know, all that gets in our way is a feeling of 'I can't handle it'.

But listen to this. If you can handle drinking to the levels you have done in the past, to blackout, to falling over, to having hangovers the devil himself would fear and have then gone back for more, you are one heck of a strong person, and can handle anything. You can handle a quit.

And rather than starting a new habit or hobby, with all the stresses, strains and potential pitfalls that entails, let your new habit be sobriety. Your new habit can be one of self-love, care and compassion for yourself. Each day you will cycle round, feeling better, thinking clearer, being proud.

Once sober and happy, you may even want to see what other amazing changes happen in your life. Above all else, though, try to remember that what you do each and every day in getting to and maintaining your quit is far more important than what you do every now and then, the big gestures. Small amounts of daily care and maintenance keep you running smoothly. It's that cycle of care that you want to achieve, as it will provide the foundations of your quit and ensure you maintain it. Quite soon, the fact that you are simply not drinking will be that care. You won't even need to do anything for it to be there.

You are not broken

Over the years I have heard so many people refer to addicts as broken, or suffering from a disease, or being somehow inherently different from the rest of the population. I really don't like this at all, for a number of reasons:

1. We are no different from anybody else.
2. We are not broken.
3. We do not have an incurable disease.

It is vitally important that we understand this, for it is essential for us to own, manage and succeed in our quits. I do realise this goes totally against some teachings, some established 'facts', and so be it. Personally, I find them most unhelpful, and from my own personal experience those teachings can even contribute to making things worse rather than better.

Digging deeper into each of these, I'll show you why. By saying we, as alcoholics, are different from everybody else makes us feel different. They label us as having addictive personalities, or weak wills or some other flaws of character. Because we can't control our drinking, they demand that we are somehow different, but how? Chop us up and you'll see nothing unusual. We are flesh and blood just like every other man, woman and child on the planet. We, like everyone else, are emotional, irrational, rational, impulsive, amusing, sad, elated. We are wholly human and inhabit the same world as everyone else.

Labelling us as somehow different does nobody any favours. It encourages people to treat us differently. Dare I say it breeds prejudice? What it also does is provide many a drinker with an excuse, a 'get out of jail free' card. You see, if we are fundamentally different, as drinkers, somehow not as human as the rest of the population, then it's not our fault that we drink, or continue to. You see, we're not like everyone else, and if that's the case there must be different rules by which we play.

So, if we are different in some way, then that's it. We are doomed. We can't change into a different species/variant of human, so there's no point in trying. So why bother attempting to quit?

Not so! Problem drinkers are every bit as human as the rest of the population. We come from all walks of life, but have a common issue. We have drunk enough of an addictive substance to become addicted. That's it, pure and simple. We did not set off in life as great boozers, unable to put the bottle down. Life happened, we drank, we enjoyed it, we went too far. Others can't get out of the gym, some collect teddy bears! In fact, isn't it great that we are all different? Nobody else looks like you, thinks like you, is you. It's the same for everyone. We are not different, we are unique.

Let's try and look at it that way. The 'different' label implies some kind of fault, but being unique is a cause for celebration! Use that thought in your quit.

Neither are we broken or beyond repair. We are simply in a difficult situation that many before us have managed to get out of. The great thing is that those that have gone before, that have escaped the clutches of alcohol, are just like us, ordinary men and women. They are not superheroes, they are office workers, factory hands, builders and lawyers, gardeners and policemen, all people just like you and me. They were not broken; maybe a little battered and bruised (and some more so than others), but they have all moved on to a better place, a place without alcohol, and we can learn from them. Each and every one, once having quit, is happier, healthier and more fulfilled in life. There's nothing broken about them. In many ways, they are stronger for it!

And for those who say we have (had?) an incurable disease, do you not realise how damaging that is?

If we take on the suggestion that we are incurable, we can feel that we will be burdened for the rest of our days. We will be ill forever and, if that's the case, we can look forward to a life of misery and sickness. This is a bleak prospect and, to be honest, not one that anybody would wish upon another. But that is exactly what those who say this is an incurable disease are condemning us to. They are telling us, quite simply, that there is no way out.

Rightly or wrongly I disagree with this, and this is why. When we drink, we are taking in a poison and it is the poison that makes us ill. It messes with our minds and it damages the tissues of our bodies. That damage it causes is the illness, and we keep it going by continually ingesting alcohol. We have become ill by inviting alcohol into our lives, and would be well had we not. This, then, is self-inflicted illness. To stop it, we should stop taking the cause of the illness: alcohol.

Rather than being an incurable disease, we can make ourselves better forever. And the prescription for this miracle cure?

Stop drinking.

Now, these two words may come across as flippant and simplistic, but I tell you one thing about them: you can. You are totally hopeless and helpless in the face of an incurable disease, but totally in control of this.

Far from being broken, you are on the first step towards full health and happiness. Set your mind to this. Shut out those who say you have an incurable disease, prove them wrong. You can, you must, and I believe you will.

For, if you are not broken, all you need to do is find the right key to lock the door on alcohol and to unlock the one to your sobriety. It is there inside you and always has been. You've had the answer with you all the time; it's part of who you are.

Fiction vs reality

One of the great advantages for those of us wanting to quit drinking is that our minds are, weirdly, unable to tell the difference between reality and fiction. There's been a ton of research done on this, so check it out if you are interested; but for the purposes of this section, let's take that as read and look to see how we can use that to our advantage.

First off, I know I used to stir up my anticipation of a drink, so much so that I was almost drunk on my own thoughts. It goes like this. The mind works first, altering its state because of the thought of alcohol, not because of its presence. Before having that first drink of an evening, many of us really look forward to it, imagining what it will be like, what it will taste like, feel like, where we will be, who we will be with. So, as we open the fridge, pull out the bottle, withdraw the cork and pour, our minds are racing ahead to that place we imagine, of relaxation and enjoyment. We pour the wine, its aroma fills our nostrils and we slowly pick up the glass. As it comes to our lips and we gently tilt the glass, our bodies are already undergoing a physiological change. We actually FEEL the weight being lifted from our shoulders; we FEEL the tension melt away.

These feelings actually happen; we change our physical state as that wine slips down. Our emotional and physical states are inextricably intertwined. We believe it's because of the wine, but it can't be. It takes a few minutes for the alcohol to get into our bloodstream and take effect. What we are experiencing is the result of our imagination, our state of mind, our emotions. It is that which has altered our physical state and we can feel it. Alcohol has no part to play at this point. It works on a time delay, which explains why we get to the point of feeling 'this is the perfect semi-drunk state I like' and always go too far. Once we actually get to feel it, we'll already have had another drink or two which have yet to take effect, but will soon push us beyond where we want be. We think we are in control, but we are not, and by then it's too late.

In a nutshell, we get drunk on the thought of alcohol before we get drunk on alcohol. Our brains get so caught up in the upcoming drink that they default to the 'I've had a drink' mode in advance of it happening. Don't you start to feel relaxed even before the drink has passed your lips? And so what? How does this help you if you regularly drink too much? In fact, isn't it great, because you can get that emotional release from stress and anxiety that much quicker!

What this shows us is that our minds and bodies don't always behave as we would expect them to. In this example we are changing physically based on an upcoming event, and anybody who has experienced the feeling of relaxation as they pour a drink will know this to be true. Over time, we have become so accustomed to it that the routine plays on autopilot. Perhaps we can use this to our advantage in quitting, maybe we can come up some new routines that will help alter our emotional state, so much so that it means we don't automatically reach for a drink to do it for us.

There are two powerful techniques that can be employed here, and I believe they serve a purpose at both ends of our quit. The first helps us imagine what MIGHT happen if we do have a drink, and so helps us in our quest to stop. The other, more useful in maintaining our quit, shows us how things will be if we don't have a drink. Each technique takes us to a new emotional state, and it is that state that will help us either quit in the first place, or remain quit over the coming days and years.

These two techniques are:

1. Play it forwards.
2. Imagine your happy place.

Let's start with play it forwards. In this one, we simply let our imagination take us to where we might end up if we have a drink, and then another, and another, and so on. I know that I have no off switch. I also know I have blackouts, and that I can behave totally irrationally when drunk. So, where *could* I end up? Maybe in a fight, beaten up. Would I drive? Maybe I'd have an accident. Maybe I'd say things I'd regret. Maybe I'd spend a night in the police cells, maybe longer depending on what I'd done.

We've all had lucky escapes when drinking, some close shaves. We've led charmed lives, but this can't carry on. One day we will get hurt, or hurt someone else in ways we can only imagine. Keep playing it forwards and we lose our jobs, family, dignity, everything. This is all in our heads, our imaginations, and all considered when we are sober, before we have had a drink. We know it to be true; we've already been down this path many times before, it's a winding path with many different outcomes, none good.

Before you have a drink, think about which path you'd like to take, and I bet you it won't be any of these. If you have already been there in your imagination, you know you don't want to go there in reality, and the great thing is you don't have to. You've already experienced the emotional horror and stress of that, and you don't need it all over again.

Instead, move on to option two, and take yourself to your happy place, a place you feel calm, serene, where you are at your most relaxed. Find a comfortable seat, sit gently and close your eyes. I take myself on a walk at this point. I'm in North Wales, by a river I love, the scene of my happiest times as a child growing up, as a young man fishing for trout, walking with my girlfriend (now wife), and showing it to my own children who, in turn, love the place. As soon as I close my eyes I am there. I can hear the river babbling away, the wind in the trees. I can smell the woodsmoke from open fires, and I am gone. I'm immediately relaxed, calm, smiling and in my own private heaven. Nowadays I go there every day for five or ten minutes. It's like a mini holiday in my head; it reminds me that life is, actually, wonderful, and mine for the taking! It's all there, and I needn't have a drink to get there. Simply using my imagination for a few minutes, relaxing, breathing deep and smooth, I immediately feel calmer, more relaxed.

Taking myself to my happy place now gives me the same buzz I used to get before pouring a glass of wine, and I get to stay sober and enjoy it whenever I want, on my terms.

We can alter our state by simply thinking about it. We can, with a very little effort, change our emotional state and with that change our desire to drink is upended. It's not going to happen immediately, it'll take a bit of practice, but it's worth sticking with.

Understand where you don't want to go by playing it forwards, and then head to your happy place to make sure you don't need a drink to live a peaceful life.

Cognitive dissonance

In earlier sections, we have seen how our minds can't differentiate between fiction and reality, so let's now dig a little deeper into the mind, and consider a phenomenon known as cognitive dissonance. Simply put, when we have conflict in our own minds we have cognitive dissonance. We truly believe one thing, yet act against it. We have inner turmoil. It is perhaps this that is the greatest enemy of the alcoholic. By achieving peace, we will be sober. Without disagreement, we will no longer drink.

Before launching into this important topic, perhaps the one that is most important in understanding how addiction works and why many people find quitting a struggle, we need to get to terms with the phrase 'cognitive dissonance'. You may or may not have come across it before and although it sounds all very grandiose and complicated, it's really a very simple concept. If I were to use the phrase 'internal conflict' or 'civil war', maybe that would make it clearer, and that's where we need to be. When we talk of cognitive dissonance, what we are describing is an internal disagreement in ourselves between what we know to be right and what we then do, how we act.

Let's take a really simple example. We all know that taking exercise is good for us. We know that for a fact, and we know that it will help us stay fit and healthy, as well as boost our immune systems to fight off disease. And yet we sit on the sofa, eat burgers whilst watching TV and the result is that, as a species, we are getting fatter and sicker. Type-2 diabetes was virtually unheard of in the 1970s; now it's one of the biggest killers on the planet. Why? Because the way we act (eat/exercise) does not correspond with what we know to be right.

Here's another one for you: we know smoking kills us, and most uncomfortably, but still many people continue to smoke.

On topic, we know that drinking alcohol kills us, and that it can lead to a most uncomfortable death, and yet we continue to drink.

When we act in a manner that is contrary to what we know, act differently from our beliefs, we are in a state of internal conflict, of cognitive dissonance:

- Cognitive – the process of knowing.
- Dissonance – lack of agreement.

And taking these together, as Wikipedia describes:

'In the field of psychology, cognitive dissonance occurs when a person holds contradictory beliefs, ideas, or values, and is typically experienced as psychological stress when they participate in an action that goes against one or more of them.'

So, when we drink we put ourselves under stress because we are drinking, and know we shouldn't be drinking. Then comes the reaction to that stress that most dependent drinkers experience, and that reaction is to turn to alcohol to relieve the very stress it caused in the first place. As you can see, we are stuck.

This is what cognitive dissonance is, and it also explains why using willpower to break an addiction is unlikely to work. Our actions, driven by instinct, are deeply ingrained in us, built up over tens of thousands of years. Our belief system and logical, analytical brain, is a recent development. Ancient instinct and modern logic do not always see eye to eye, and they even reside in totally different physical areas of our brain. When we try to use our willpower, driven by logic and thought, against instinct, driven by survival, there will always be one winner – instinct.

Unless we work on that instinct, the ancient brain it resides in and how it works, then we will always find quitting hard. However, once we have worked on it, and got it to understand that it is better not to drink than it is to drink for our long and short-term survival, then quitting will be easy. Yes, I'll use that sentence: 'Quitting will be easy.' Getting there involves hard work, but the results are magnificent, success feels good, and we all like to feel good I'm sure. You see, we drank to make ourselves feel better than we did before, even if that was just to shut out bad things – we drank, or still drink, to feel good.

The question then comes, how can we change our instinctive brain? For, if it is instinctive, it surely works on autopilot. In a sense, we need to reprogramme it. Much of what it believes to be true, and uses to drive our behaviour, has been built up over our lifetime of experiences. What we have found during the course of this book is that we are influenced by society, our friends, advertising, TV, radio and so on, and that we as humans are social animals and want to fit in. Going against the grain means you will not be welcome in the tribe and, in terms of survival, Stone Age loners died. Safety and security and survival was gained from being in the group. Being inundated with images of alcohol providing that group, the ancient brain locks on and makes it our survival driver. We enter that tribe of drinkers, and feel safe, secure and at home.

Our ancient brain has learned this, found it to be true through early experience, without us even noticing. In a nutshell, we now have a part of our brain that will demand we drink alcohol for our own good.

Alongside this comes logic. In our conscious, logical, thinking brain we go something like, 'I really should stop drinking. I know it's not good for me, but every time I try I end up drinking again. This is stupid – why can't I just stop?'

The reason you can't stop? Your ancient, survival brain, demands you drink in order to remain safe, to remain alive, to stay in the group, for your own good. Yes, you drink in order to keep alive! Trying to quit without understanding and re-educating your ancient brain is therefore a direct threat to your very survival, and thus will fail.

This is why using willpower to quit will not work.

So let's end on some good news, shall we? And it is this. Our ancient brain, our survival brain, has been able to learn from society, TV and so on. Therefore it is not fixed, which means that it can learn again. We can re-educate it, re-programme it and thus remove its drive to alcohol as a survival choice. And even better, once we have performed that reset, quitting will become the most natural thing in the world. We will simply not want to drink, our desire will be gone, and we will not have to make any effort to stop. Not drinking will be our new survival default.

Remove that internal conflict, that cognitive dissonance, and a sober calm will prevail.

Wants and needs

Hiding the truth about your drinking isn't really the issue, it's the need that you have to drink that does the harm. More damaging still, it's not even that you really 'want' to drink, it's a 'need' that you have, and that is a lot more pernicious.

A need is something you have to have to survive or complete a task. A want is simply the desire for something.

There's a world of difference between these in the cycle of addiction, in the descent into alcohol abuse and dependence, rather than the simple enjoyment of alcohol that so many seem to live by.

To see the problem more clearly, it's important to understand why we have needs and what drives them. As you can see from my statement above, a need is about survival. Deep inside our brains there resides a small, ancient part of our primitive brain, a part that has the single job of keeping us alive, safe and well. This is the amygdala, and it runs quite happily without our even being aware of it. It ensures we stay alive.

This ancient brain makes sure we drink when we are thirsty and eat when we are hungry, and keeps our bodies in balance, in a state of homeostasis. It makes sure we get enough sleep, that we produce the right hormones and antibodies to stay well, to fight off disease and so on. It even regulates our temperature. Without it we would not last long. This part of our brain doesn't engage in thinking, it just *does*. It works on one level, our level of need, and nowhere else. It senses what we need to keep in balance, and drives us to maintain that, whatever it might be.

We don't get the 'I have to have a chocolate, and I have to have it now' feeling from nowhere! We are being driven to it by that ancient brain and there's something in that chocolate that will restore our bodily balance. We literally need it and, whatever happens, we will get it. From time to time, I may fancy a chocolate, I may 'want' one but at that level it doesn't become all-consuming, and I can quite easily do without.

So, what has fancying a chocolate got to do with the cycle of addiction, and where does alcohol come into it? And if wants and needs are so different, one being aspirational and the other critical to survival, how is it that we can't keep away from the drink when it is absolutely NOT helping with our survival, and we DON'T want to drink anyway?

There are two answers here:

1. It's a chemical thing.
2. We learn.

In the chemical arena, I'm sure we can all agree that alcohol is an addictive substance. If we take an addictive substance into our bodies we will, given time and enough exposure, become addicted. It does not matter who we are or what we do, how strong we are or where we come from, we are all the same underneath, and any single one of us could become addicted.

Addiction is illogical on the surface, but dig a little deeper and it makes absolute sense. Moving on from the accepted truth that we get addicted to addictive substances, because of their chemical nature, how does the fact that we learn come into the equation? In fact, the more we drink, the more we learn that it's not good for us, that it is damaging in so many ways, so surely what we learn should drive us away from, rather than towards, drinking?

Maybe, but for now, let's travel into the realms of the hangover, find out what we have learned from drinking, and then see where this learning has taken place and set root. For this journey we need to head back into the amygdala, that part of the brain we have been introduced to that does all the good work keeping us alive, in balance, without our needing to intervene. Remember, too, that this part of the brain doesn't think, it merely does. Created over tens of thousands of years, not thinking has its advantages – it conserves vital energy and it means there is no delay in avoiding danger – we react immediately, unthinkingly. This keeps us alive much better than wondering what to do when faced with imminent danger – such as a sabre-toothed tiger attack!

What this part of the brain can also do is learn by experience. It learns that certain actions and behaviours help keep us in balance and keep us alive. When we see a red light when out driving, we don't need to think what that means, we know. It becomes second nature. Humans didn't evolve with traffic lights, but this part of our brain is there to keep us alive, and can learn how best to do that. If it takes away our need to consider what to do when driving towards a red light, we'll stop safely without needing to think about it.

Returning to our hangover, we really don't like feeling this way. We are totally out of sorts, out of balance. As a heavy, long-term or even binge drinker, what we really want is to feel normal again. Normal. That's it. That's what we say to ourselves, what we promise ourselves as we say 'never again', yet again. And deep inside our brains that little, ancient part, the amygdala, has the single job of keeping us in balance, feeling normal, as it were. It has also learned that when we feel this way, when we are down, scared, hungover, stressed, sad, emotionally unstable or otherwise out of balance, a drink will help us. For a hangover we call it hair of the dog. A drink will help take the edge off it at least. We know this works (short term). We know we feel better for it. We have learned it at the deepest level.

When we feel the debilitating after-effects of alcohol, it is the job of the amygdala to restore balance. It will resort to what it has learned over the years of our drinking. It knows from experience that when we feel this way, we turn to booze, and that it makes us feel better. It does not think, nor does it judge; it merely sends out an order, that we must fulfil a need. That need is to restore balance, and to satisfy this need the answer is to drink alcohol. It is as simple, to that unthinking brain, and as obvious as eating is to satisfy hunger. The drive to satisfy that is no want, no wish or dream. It is an imperative, it is an absolute survival need.

Once the chemical process has got us addicted, and we start using alcohol to help us get through life, to cope with it, then that learning is set in motion. Eventually, it becomes automated, and what was once a want (a drink on a Friday night) now becomes a need (a drink just to feel normal).

There is good news though. Because the amygdala has a capability to learn, we can teach it more productive ways, and steer it, over time, away from the 'need' for alcohol. We can replace the need with something healthier, or remove it altogether, which I prefer. We will then be rid of that 'need' to drink, which you feel as an insatiable craving, even when we know it's a really bad idea. Once rid of that need, balance is quickly restored by nature, and the amygdala will soon enough stop sending out demands for booze! Without those demands, you won't have to resist them, and life will become altogether more peaceful. With this peace our 'want' for a drink will also fade away, and our quit will strengthen day by day.

We can thereby show the world that we are not broken, and that we are in control, despite what people seem to think.

Filters

Do we ever see the world as it really is? Will we ever know? Do we miss stuff?

A falcon has better precision eyesight than we have, owls can see in ultraviolet, and our range of hearing is limited. So yes, we do miss stuff, and lots of it. We are biologically incapable of seeing, hearing and sensing certain things. Sharks detect the tiny pulses of electricity that fish's muscles give off when they swim, to hunt and catch them. We certainly haven't got that superpower!

We are made just right, though. Our senses are honed to what we need to survive, developed over millions of years. We have just the right level of sight, hearing, taste, touch and smell to help us thrive. And we have the brains to process this, up to a point. Every second of every day we are bombarded with images, sounds and so on. We can't possibly take it all in – we'd frazzle. Out of these billions of bits of data coming our way, the vast majority is filtered out.

At a party, we are aware of all the chatter, but only hear the words of the person we are speaking to. We can drive a familiar route, commuting to work for example, and recall virtually none of it on arrival. To make sense of what is around us, pick out what matters and what does not, our brains set up filters, only allowing certain information through. That way we can cope. These filters make sure signs of danger are always let through, important messages are picked up, and we stay safe and well. We never miss overhearing our own name, do we?

Every one of us filters what comes in, and all our filters are different. We all see the world slightly, sometimes radically, different from everyone else. Often enough, we are both correct.

Our filters drive our perception of reality and, as it is our perception that we aware of, that is our reality.

These filters and subsequent perceptions that create our reality are not only innate, but learned. Indeed, over time, filters have become the way in which mankind has developed and maintained society. And, as much as filters can be learned, like stop at a red light, they can also be taught.

Advertisers, influencers, and manipulators all work in this area, repeating messages and signals that we, unconsciously, build into our values. I'm not just talking about professionals here, but our parents, friends, associates, and whether they do it deliberately or not.

There is nothing inherently wrong with four letters in a row, is there?

F-U-C-K

Maybe there is? Our filter, our way of accepting that word into our minds was not there when we were born. We have learned it, been taught it, and built it into our values, our filters. Early on, we know the word 'FUCK' as a bad word. Likewise, we are told, accept, and take on board many other things as good things. With these we build our values, which drive our view of the world.

And so it is with alcohol. Much of what we see of alcohol is through a portrayal of fun, excitement and friendship. It is the world's oldest social lubricant, it helps break the ice, and keeps conversations going. Not only that, it tastes great – well, as an ingredient, not on its own. It's like garlic that way; we don't eat it raw, on its own, and nor do we glug pure alcohol. Actually, that would kill us pretty fast if we did. Alcohol has so much going for it. It relaxes us, de-stresses us, makes us sexier, chattier, braver even. It helps us put our problems to one side.

It destroys our liver. It empties our wallets. It loses us our driving licences. It causes divorces. It leads to violence.

Filter time!

When we drink, all those home truths are shut out. How could we possibly enjoy a drink with all those thoughts and images coming in with it? They're all out there, but we find them uncomfortable. We don't consider the death of thousands of brain cells with each sip of whisky, do we? Of course not. We are made to survive, be safe, and live peacefully. We filter out what does not contribute to this state, and thus the dark and unpleasant truths about alcohol don't get through. We can enjoy a drink.

'Yes, I know. I don't want to hear it.'

That's right. We've all heard that one, haven't we? Said it, too, no doubt, at some time or other, maybe more than once. When our filters don't work, or can't, we are confronted by the truth, generally pointed out by a well-meaning friend who kindly points out, 'Drinking's only going to make it worse, you know.' Thanks, pal, I know that and do NOT want to be reminded! Not just a filter this time, a deliberate block.

The question we need to address when we look at our filters is whether they help us or hinder us. Without doubt, those that cause us to behave in a civilised manner, avoid sensory overload and guide us through life are helpful. There are others that we also believe do that, but become warped over time. Bad habits develop, and we filter out and become unaware of the damage they do to us and to others. Sit back and you know, without much effortful thought, which are which. You know that a filter that puts you in denial of the fact that what you are doing is very harmful is not doing you a favour at all.

Don't you reckon we need to change these filters? If we think of them like the lenses in a pair of sunglasses, consider how quickly our view of the world changes when we swap blue lenses for pink. The change is immediate, and achieved simply. Perhaps, when looking to quit alcohol, a quick change of filter will help us. Maybe allowing a touch of reality through the filter will help us take a moment, and pause, before we decide to have a drink.

As we've seen before, taking a moment to pause can be a powerful tool in developing your quit. It's simple, too. And when combined with an understanding of our filters, might well be one of the building blocks of your quit.

Change your filter – Change your perception – Change your reality.

To die for

Maybe this is the phrase of the early 21st century. It's all simply divine, that dessert was *to die for,* that dress was *to die for.* We're surrounded by things that are to die for, meaning simply that something is excellent, or that you would do anything to get it. It seems that so much is to die for these days, so is it really all so excellent?

I was having a chat in our local park at the weekend, with a good friend who had just been a little unwell, and had thus spent some time watching daytime TV as he was recovering. He had, in fact, quit drinking a few years ago 'to find out what it felt like', discovered that it felt great, and thus hasn't drunk since. He, too, is really interested in other people's stories about drinking and quitting, and also wants to write about it. As we were talking, we got on to the fact that we were so happy to be fit and well with all this Covid-19 going on around us, and that exercising is so important to our health. He then brought up a TV interview he had seen a few days before, with a previously alcoholically drinking woman being interviewed. In it, he recalled this woman questioning the phrase 'to die for', and asking why so many people would be willing to die for a piece of cake, but when it came to quitting drinking, were barely able 'to live for' their own children.

It seems people are willing 'to die for' all sorts of things to live even remotely happily. Is it any wonder we are so messed up?

Much of what people say they are willing 'to die for' is of no true value, will not make a positive and lasting change in the way in which they live their lives, and yet they say they would lay down our lives for them. And our brains listen to this, and hear it over and over and over again. Drummed into us, relentlessly, we come to believe this false value as true. This is what life becomes: false.

But what if we were to turn it on its head? What if we were to say something was 'to live for'? What is worth living for? Oddly enough, when we dig a little deeper, just below the surface, we find there all sorts of different things, but predominantly, when we say we 'live for' something, that something is love, helping someone else, enthusiasm in simply being. 'To live for' is to experience, to feel, to have a permanence in an ever-changing world.

All that is 'to die for' will, itself, die. If something is worth living for, it will be there forever. When we decide to quit drinking, we move ourselves away from a life of 'I'm dying for a drink', to one in which we see new ways and experiences 'to live for'.

And here's the dilemma. In order to quit we know we need to be incredibly selfish, that it is our quit, and that we should be doing it for ourselves and nobody else. But if we are 'to live for' our children (read also parents, family, friends), then are we not quitting for someone else? And if we are quitting for someone else, then we are less likely to succeed, or remain successful.

It's all a matter of perspective. From our (the quitters') perspective, we are able to watch our children grow up, enjoy the company of our friends, have new experiences we would never have if we were still drinking, or had decided that these were not 'to live for'. By choosing this direction we have opened ourselves up to life at its best. From everyone else's perspective we are now there for them. We are a positive part of their lives, providing love, fun and a solid foundation for them. Sober, we become reliable, trustworthy, loving and loved. These are no mere trinkets, these are life itself.

And I can promise you, from the moment you quit, these are the things that will start growing in your life. They will strengthen every day, confirming you made the right choice, strengthening you and your quit. Previously, you may have been willing 'to die for' a drink, but moving forwards, you'll want 'to live for' the great new experiences that every day will bring you. OK, not every day will be brilliant; life just isn't like that. Sober, you'll ride out these not-so-good days as a bump in the road, then crack on again the next day, seeing what there is 'to live for' in that one.

To switch from one to another, maybe we need a little reprogramming.

Hard coded or configurable?

This is one way I find works really well for describing people and their drinking habits. The aim of this section is to show you how, for your drinking, to put your body and mind back to 'factory settings'. Think about it the way you would if your laptop started going wrong. You may call the IT Helpdesk and, chances are they'll tell you to 'turn it off and on again'. It usually works.

How about we apply that level of simplicity of thinking and acting to our quit?

Let's say we were to turn you off and on again, and we could set you and your drinking back to where it was before you even started. You would have been returned to 'factory settings', the way you were when you were born into this world. We could then ensure that as you developed, and you were configured to live in the modern world; drinking was simply not in the 'requirements'. Without these there would be no programming, and you wouldn't drink. Much like a computer without code telling it to do something, you would be set up not to drink, no matter what.

Try to put that image in your mind, doing a mental reset, leaving out some unhelpful instructions and, hey presto, you won't drink again! The steps to do this are really very simple, require little or no effort to understand, and are there for the taking. All you need to do is allow the concept of returning yourself to factory settings to settle into your mind, and get used to that idea. Further, as you have 'learned' to drink, what's to stop you unlearning or, rather, not re-learning to once you have done the reset?

162

What we need to understand first is that our brains learn all the time, and they try to work as efficiently as possible. By the way, they use up loads of power – something like 20% of our calorie burn is in our brains! Thus, over time, if we think and do things regularly enough, high-speed links are made in the brain so that thought no longer precedes action. This is efficiency. Rather than deciding what to do every time a situation occurs, the path is already laid out. It becomes hard coded (hard wired). As a result, we reach for a drink without thought when we go to the pub, eat a meal, feel stressed, get angry, are bored, watch TV. There is a simple trigger, we take a pre-determined action.

This Trigger > Action response makes so much sense. It is borne out of our need to survive, and this lends itself to hard coding. If you wait to think and decide what to do out of a series of options, you could be dead – eaten by a sabre-toothed cat! Instead, don't think – just RUN!

It is this that we need to work on, and fortunately it's something that is, practically, really simple. For this to work, we can put in a diversion, like workmen do for roadworks, as it is very much the same concept. When it comes to driving and roadworks, we are used to getting from A to B along a certain road. It has become second nature. Put in a diversion, and we have to think where we are going, we need to concentrate and follow the road signs. We are no longer on autopilot and arriving at our destination, sometimes without even noticing the journey. We've all done that haven't we? We have all driven a familiar route and have no recollection of it, or major parts of it, once it's over. It just happened naturally. But put in some roadworks and we become conscious of it all over again, and need to make decisions, be alert to what we are doing and where we are going.

This works just as well for our brains, with a little effort. To stop us hitting the superfast neural pathway from event to drink, Trigger > Action, we simply put in a question or two before we pour or sip our drink. What those questions are is entirely up to you; the idea is simply to cause disruption. If we force a question often enough, and it won't take too long, our new natural reaction will be to pause. We will have built a new habit, and this pause will be enough for us to question that drink, to give our desire to quit a chance to wave its flag and say 'remember me?' Once reminded, we won't forget, and the chances are we will give that drink a miss.

Triggers

In the past, we have been told to remove or avoid the trigger and we won't drink, or we'll find it easier not to. That may be so, but there will be occasions we can't avoid the trigger or, if you are like me, you'll become so obsessed about avoiding triggers that you won't be able to do anything else! Or your life becomes so dull because you have to stop doing everything because there's an associated trigger! That's no good, is it?

So how about this instead? Relax, accept that triggers exist, allow them in, but give them a big yellow 'Diversion' sign. Treat every different trigger the same and your life will be so much simpler. You'll only ever have to think one thing: Trigger > Diversion. That diversion could be as simple as 'Wait in a queue for five minutes.' The chances are that in five minutes, your triggered urge to drink will have gone.

You have changed your neural pathway. Rather than being hard coded as you thought, it is actually configurable. It was configured through your life to drive you to drink, and now you have stepped in, performed a reset, and reconfigured it. And once your diversion has set its own pathway up, any triggers will simply head off down the route to being forgotten. You won't notice them, and quitting will come naturally.

Car maintenance

Now that my car is three years old, I take it for its annual MOT. Not only is it illegal to drive without this basic check, I also have the peace of mind that my car is fundamentally safe to drive. As well as this, I carry out other checks on a regular basis. I ensure that it is serviced regularly, to keep it running smoothly, and replace worn parts as and when necessary. When warning lights come on, I see to it that I get the underlying issue fixed. As I rely on my car to get me around, it's important that it's in good working order at all times.

As well as regular check-ups to ensure my car is good to go, I also make sure it has the right fuel in it, and I confirm the oil is topped up. Without these, I won't get very far! Basically, I make sure I look after my car properly, so it does what I need it to do, reliably.

Can you say the same for yourself when you are drinking? Are you looking after your health? Are you feeding yourself properly? Are you taking in the right fluids for optimum performance? No way! If you neglected your car as you did yourself, and fed it the wrong fuels, it would have broken down long ago. And yet, as people, not only do we abuse ourselves past any reasonable point, but we also manage to keep on going regardless.

Sitting here watching the snow fall outside my office window at home, I'm just arranging for my car to go back at the end of its lease. I'm also in the process of finding a new one, as it will need to do some serious towing in the summer and beyond, and the one I have now isn't up to the job. That's the beauty of cars as well, isn't? When one wears out or becomes unsuitable, we can simply get a new one. If our car is no longer for us, we replace it.

But we can't do that with our bodies. We have this one to live in, and this one alone. We can't change it. Maybe, with extreme difficulty, we can change bits of it with transplants, but this isn't really an option for those of us who abuse ourselves to death, quite literally. Your average drunk won't get a liver transplant – there are, quite rightly, plenty more deserving folk ahead of us in the queue – and we will die before one ever comes along.

Our bodies are machines. They need care and maintenance; they need looking after like any other machine. We should feed them what they need for optimal performance, look after them through suitable exercise and rest, and also take care of their software systems – meaning the brain, or rather, the thoughts that go on in there! Well maintained, our bodies will last and last. They will change over time of course, but we'll always be fine in them while they are well cared for.

Let them fall apart like a rusting and neglected car, and they'll be a horrible place to be. Aches, pains, negative thoughts, and illnesses will become the norm. Eventually, parts will stop working; we'll suffer badly with heart conditions, organ failures and so on.

The manual for looking after our bodies is far simpler than the one for a car. Mechanics train for years to understand how a car works and work out what to fix when things go wrong. We don't need to. Cut out the booze, eat a reasonably mixed variety of food and drink and move about a bit, that'll do! That's a fairly easy manual to master, isn't it? And it really is all there is to it, more especially because the better you feel, the more settled your mind will be. As they say:

Healthy body, healthy mind.

One really does lead to another, and both lead us away from drinking alcohol.

Make sure you know the manual for optimum human performance and you'll be OK!

And here it is:

- Eat well.
- Move well.
- Sleep well.

A six-word manual – who'd have thought?

Chatter

I don't know if you are like me, but I've got this incessant chattering going on in my brain. Chatter, chatter, all day long, it never stops, it just keeps going. Even when my head hits the pillow, my mind still races; it seems to have boundless energy.

Half the time I don't recall what it's talking about, but given the chance it will grab my attention. It's interesting to note when this takes place, when it grabs my attention, what I used to do, and what I now do about it. Let's put it simply. When I was in a generally good mood, I really didn't take much notice of any self-talk. When I was down in the dumps, I'd often dive straight in and join the conversation.

My reaction to any self-talk was largely determined by my emotional state at the time, even though the thoughts that would come and go would largely be the same. If I was down, I'd sink deeper with them. If I was up, they would pass me by.

On doing some extra research, reading around, I soon discovered that all our thoughts behave in a similar way. They rise up from deep within, come to the surface, grow like balloons, and then pop as if they were bubbles in a hot, volcanic mud pool. Like these mud bubbles, our thoughts will simply pop and be gone, only to be replaced by a new one, even several at a time. Like the chatter in our minds, these bubbles never stop.

So what can we learn from a volcanic pool? Keeping it simple, we can reduce this to one simple lesson. If we ignore the bubble, the thought, it will go away. Nobody and nothing dwells in the mud pool. However, if we dwell on our thoughts, keeping them alive, they grow and grow far beyond their natural state. All other mud bubbles simply pop.

Our thoughts are, by their very nature, both transient and wholly dependent on our reaction to them for their survival. How much control we have over which thoughts make it to the surface and we notice is beyond what we will look at here, so let's accept they come from deep within, without our intervention. It is likely that we will have happy thoughts when we are feeling good, and sadder thoughts when we are in a melancholy state.

Understanding that we really have no control over our thoughts, but that we do have control over how we react to them is a key realisation. We now know that thoughts come and go, and that they do not last if they are not dwelt upon. A plant without water will wither and die, and a thought ignored will, too.

Now that we know how turning our attention to a thought will nurture it, make it grow, it also goes that if we turn away from a thought it will perish. Thoughts come and go all the time, they are not long lived, so when starved of attention they don't hang around. It's not as if you need to ignore them for very long – they'll soon be gone.

But the question now comes as to how we ignore a thought. After all, when we are told NOT to think about a pink elephant, all we can think about and can see in our mind's eye is a pink elephant. The more we make an effort to ignore something the more it dominates us. To starve a thought, please don't go about it by saying, 'I must not think this way, I must take no notice of this.' You'll only drive yourself nuts! Rather, for the matter of a few seconds, take a few deep calming breaths, imagine a place of peace and calm, if needed force a happy memory or image of your favourite place to the front of your mind and imagine being there, calm, content and relaxed. I take myself to North Wales. I see the rocks and crags, the greens and brown of grass and heather, the silver threads of waterfalls, and feel the fresh breeze on my face. I don't need to be there for long to have that negative thought fade away. I come back from my mental trip to North Wales in a state of emotional peace and relaxation. And when I'm in that state, negative thoughts don't even arise.

I know it may sound corny, but give it a go. As well as quashing unwelcome thoughts, mental tourism also stops them coming up in the first place. It does become easier over time and, as I've said, these thoughts only really hang around for a matter of seconds, so let them die a natural death: or, if they need killing, starvation is best!

And the best thing? Once you quit drinking, you'll feel so much better physically, mentally and emotionally that these bubbling thoughts will surface less and less often, even as you get better and better at dealing with them. By understanding how thoughts come and go, as well as having a simple defence mechanism, which you'll use less and less as time goes by, you now have an even better chance of quitting when you feel the time is right for you. Don't wait until the time is perfect, just do it when it's right! You'll know when that is and, with the right backup and knowledge, specific to you, you'll crack it.

DECIDING TO QUIT

Do not try until you are ready

Most of us who drink too much want to stop, or at least cut down. And let's be honest, if we want to cut down we don't really want to stop and, if that's the case, you'll not cut down. You'll still 'enjoy' a drink and you'll find it so hard to limit your intake that you'll want to have a drink because of that! If your aim is to cut down, then you are not ready to quit. So don't try. Which do you want?

On the whole, we can't go from full-blown dependent drinker (alcoholic drinker) to teetotaller overnight. Nobody does this without having spent time thinking about it, at least. I would say it's just about impossible to make the decision and then stop immediately, permanently and easily, with no preparation or planning. It just doesn't work that way.

Let's consider a simple analogy: driving.

I would imagine that a fair proportion of you drive, and we'll all know someone who does, so this should be relatively straightforward. One day, some time ago, you or they were unable to drive. Again, at some point, you will have made a decision – 'I want to drive' – and set your sights on getting that all important driver's licence. You will not have decided, then simply walked off, grabbed a set of keys and driven away, a fully competent driver. Of course not. We all know that would simply not work, that there's an awful lot more to it than that.

So instead you put on the L-plates, hire an instructor and learn.

In order to drive a car, we need to understand all sorts of manoeuvres. We need to understand how to operate all the controls, learn the *Highway Code*, and be aware of the way other drivers behave on the roads. We learn how to anticipate what will happen next. We then need to put all this together at the same time when we are out on the road.

And only once we have mastered all these are we ready to put them into practice and take our driving test. All being well, we PASS! We pass not because we have made a decision, but because we have acted upon it and put the necessary pieces in place to make that decision a success.

And it is the same with quitting alcohol. There is a gap between making the decision and it coming to life, wouldn't you agree?

Sometimes that can happen quite quickly, other times it can take a bit longer. And I have found there are no shortcuts. You can't force the issue. That will, inevitably, backfire. If you try and quit before you are ready you are likely to fail, much like you are likely to crash a car if you start driving before you have learned how. Such failures or crashes can get you down and you may well drink to push away the disappointment. You need to put in the work before quitting. Not doing so can be profoundly counterproductive, and lead to a worse outcome than if you'd simply waited. One way I tried was in a quit clinic, but not until I had spent some time in AA.

First stop, AA

I was given such a kind welcome when I first turned up at Alcoholics Anonymous (AA), one Wednesday evening in April, all those years ago. Nervous and feeling awkward, I was one of two new faces that evening, and the two of us were to become good friends after that. On arriving, one of the members took it upon himself to come over, introduce himself, lead me inside for a coffee and generally make me feel welcome. Not much was said about why I was there, what had made me start that day; the important thing to everyone was that I WAS there, that I had come out that evening. It was as if I were being told 'Don't worry, you're home now,' and it made me feel safe.

I was also struck by the other people in the room, and to this day I still am. Expecting a group of brown-paper-baggers, society's cast-offs and undesirables, I was instead faced with a room of well-spoken, respectable, intelligent and thoughtful individuals. Everyone was polite, kind, well-dressed and on time! It all shouted out, 'It's OK here, don't worry, we are quite normal people, just like you.' Of course, the common thread running through the group was that everyone had or had had a drink problem so severe that they sought the help of the world's biggest and best-known self-help group, AA. And by the look of it, they were all doing very well from it.

All I recall of that first meeting was being greeted, where I sat in the room, and just listening. I realised I was not alone, that I was not the only middle-class, middle manager with a decent job, car, family and so on that had an alcohol problem. There were other people just like me in there, as well as builders, accountants, nurses: you name them, they were there, or are in a room somewhere around the world. Alcohol does not target anyone, it gets everyone. That first meeting set me on a path to many more.

I loved it, made friends, had laughs, shed some tears, did 'service' (helping organise coffee and tea, room layout, meetings, sharers and so on), and told my own story a few times in 'shares'. I became a part of the furniture for quite a while, and was successfully keeping off the drink. Not everyone was, but that's OK, because the only requirement for membership is a desire to stop drinking. And there was absolutely no judgement. Drinking can't be treated that way and never, ever is in AA. Looking back, it was a special time in my life.

That's right, it *was*, past tense. I stopped going after a while, around a year or so. My experiences with AA, what I learned from it, and the wonderful people I met there remain with me. They are also, whether they are aware of it or not, a huge part of what gave me the strength to quit. Without AA it's almost certain I wouldn't have stopped drinking how and when I did. However, AA wasn't the complete answer for me, it was a piece of the jigsaw.

So what was it that made me walk away, after all the good it had done me? Fortunately, I find that very easy to answer, and I think it's important to tell you. Remember, this is simply my view, my experience; it is absolutely subjective. We all have our take on things, and we are neither right nor wrong. There is no criticism or judgement here, just what I saw and found in my own heart and mind.

So, here goes, these are three things that I personally struggled with:

- Shares
- God

- Addiction

Shares are an integral part of each of the meetings I attended, where a member will tell their story of where they were, what happened, and where they are now. We all listen intently, seeking similarities with our own lives, not differences, and then share back. Tragedy, hilarity, joy and sadness filled these shares. They were an amazing view of human life against a backdrop of alcoholism, and I learned so much from them. Over time, however, I picked up that at each and every meeting we obviously discussed alcohol and the problems we all had with it. Some had it worse than others, although there was no competition. But day in, day out, week in, week out, the topic was the same, the stories were the same. What did I expect? This was a group called AA – alcohol was their thing!

But I needed to get away from alcohol, not hear about and be reminded of it every day. My mind was still filled with alcohol, the word would never leave me, it was constantly brought to the front of my mind, and I didn't want it there. I simply wanted it gone, I wanted it to be a non-issue. In AA, it was, by the very nature of the organisation, the only issue. Going to AA only served to keep alcohol (mentally) so very close to me, and I could keep going only so long.

I gave it a break for a while, then tried going back. It hadn't changed, and neither should it have done.

God

AA is a spiritual programme of recovery, but even so I

was surprised to see the word 'God' everywhere. On posters (the 12 Steps and 12 Traditions), in the Serenity Prayer, in literature and on quotes pinned to the walls at meetings. There is no escaping God at an AA meeting. Members always said to ignore the word 'God' and go with the meaning, the intention, but I found that hard. I understand that I'm not the only one, and over time it came to be a little overwhelming, maybe unfairly cult-like, to me. I know the spiritual aspect works for so many, that the God thing isn't a problem for some, but personally, I struggled too much with it.

Maybe these two factors alone wouldn't have caused me to leave AA had it not been for the third, one that I will call...

Addiction

That's right, starting with the suggestion that we should attend 90 meetings in 90 days once we join AA, to dire warnings should we leave, I soon fell into a habit of going to meetings whenever I could. I was attending four, five, maybe even six a week, and started travelling to other towns to visit other groups. After a little while, I found that I was restless at home in the evenings if I wasn't at a meeting. I'd feel as if something was missing. I'd started to crave meetings. I'd spend all my time at them, I was neglecting the people at home. I'd quit drinking for a better life, one not taken up with drink and selfishness. Yet here I was, disappearing every night, not seeing my own family, being selfish all over again. In order to keep off the booze, I'd become addicted to AA. AA had moved from being Alcoholics Anonymous and had become Another Addiction.

177

AA – Another Addiction?

In business coaching terms, it would be called dependency. This occurs when a client finds that he or she needs their coach as a friend or ally, and aches for that professional relationship to continue and grow. The business or executive coach will have been hired for a particular job, but this then morphs into something else. The client feels they are unable to stand on their own two feet. It is, in this situation, where the hired coach needs to fire their employer! It is for the client's own good, and needs to be carried out carefully, but it must happen.

In the example above, where the client has become dependent on the coach, there is an addiction in play. For the addiction to be broken, the coach must act. But when it comes to an addiction to a substance, alcohol, the substance will not, cannot, act. This action must come from the addict.

There's a saying that once you have been to AA you'll never be able to drink the same way again. I'd agree. Virtually every day since that first meeting I have thought of AA as I picked up a drink. In the end I put the drink down, and AA had played a part in that. The people I had met there all played a part. It was just that I found AA couldn't do it all for me, so let me tell you a little more of my experiences there.

I was a member for around a year, and found the meetings enlightening, entertaining at times, and always thought provoking. The people there were absolutely lovely, supportive, understanding and, in the main, sober. Some had just got sober, some old-timers were veterans of 50 or more years' sobriety. They had seen it all and showed immense kindness and love in helping others. I felt welcome from the very start, greeted at the door by 'Young David'.

I met 'Baldy John', 'Scottish John', 'Brummie Steve', 'Tall Paul', 'Jesus Paul' and a whole host of characters. Outside of the rooms there was no way of believing these were a bunch of recovering alcoholics. They were, and are, a perfectly normal, bright and cheerful group of friends. I think this is what is so appealing, and such a relief about AA; the people there are not some bunch oddballs, they are just like everyone else, only wiser! And so it was that I found myself attending meetings on a regular basis, doing some 'service' and keeping sober. It was as if I had found a new home and a social scene I enjoyed.

Over time, I felt I was becoming a regular member of our local AA, even though I was a mere baby compared with some. I started to take it a little for granted but also felt that there were a few things about it that just didn't sit well with me. I'd tried to push them to the back of my mind, but couldn't keep them there.

As well as finding the shares an increasing issue, and struggling to come to terms with "God", I also struggled with commitment.

You see, in order to stay sober, I needed to keep going to meetings. It was drilled into me that if I were to leave the rooms and drink again, calamity would strike, that life would spiral out of control and everything would be worse than ever. So, fear kept me going back. I was going to meetings multiple times a week. Oh, I was committed all right; I wanted to quit and this was working. I also faced a dilemma. I may have put the drink down at this point, but I was never at home. I never saw my wife and children in the evenings. I was always at AA. And the prospect of going to meetings three or four times a week for the rest of my life didn't appeal either. What was the point of quitting alcohol only to spend every night away from the family, again?

So, unfortunately, I was put off AA. The idea of a life spent in the rooms really did not appeal. But mainly, looking back on it, the fault was mine. I wasn't fully ready to quit. I was desperate and this worked in the short term. I had needed to make a show, an effort, but for my family, not for me. I knew I had to quit, to find a way, and this was what I chose to start me off, in the immediate term, anyway. Maybe, just maybe, without the God stuff, I would have stayed. I'll never know, and life is about looking forwards now, not backwards.

What I can tell you is this. Without AA, without 'Baldy John' and the crew, and without what I learned in those rooms over a period of around a year, I wouldn't have been able to quit as I did when I did. AA got under my skin, somehow or other. It was something I couldn't have done without, but as a long-term solution it wasn't going to work for me. As I've said before and will say again, we are all different people and we'll all have different ways out of our problem drinking.

For me, AA was a critical stopover, rather than the destination.

Maybe, with all the hype surrounding AA as the biggest and most successful international quitting method, I really expected it to work for me, right away. In the end, it took a few more attempts, some serious and most half-hearted, to get there.

So I left, and life was bumpy after that. Things did get worse as had been predicted, but eventually they got a whole lot better.

Leaving AA was right for me at the time. It has also given me so much to be thankful for, helped my quit immeasurably, and remains right up there as one of the most powerful quitting techniques there is. I may not be an AA lifer, but I know, in spite of the difficulties I had handling it, it helped save mine.

Allen Carr was also a major factor in getting me to my eventual quit.

Allen Carr Quit Clinic

I think it might be quite useful if I were to give you a bit of personal insight into some of the things I tried as methods to quit, before I finally got here, got sober. The really good thing about all these is that there is actually a really wide choice of stuff out there that can be done. Like many people, I was blinkered into thinking that AA and rehab were pretty much the only options when it came to helping us quit drinking. I was very wrong. In the end it was a combination of a number of methods, that I pieced together myself, that enabled me to quit drinking once and for all. You may find that this works for you, too, or that just one method does it for you. Like so much in life, there is no 'one size fits all' to getting sober.

Around ten years ago, I quit smoking. I'd tried patches and e-cigs, but not much else. The NHS wasn't any use to me, and promotions like National No-Smoking Day wound me up no end! A chance conversation over the garden wall with a student renting a room next door led to his suggesting I try Allen Carr's Easyway® method to quit. He passed over a pirated video he had, and I bought the book. Immediately, I was taken by the approach, even though the language and style was a little dated. I watched and watched, read and read. I loved it. But still I smoked. I had a feeling inside me that this was the way for me, but I just needed a little more.

That little more was a day-long immersive workshop, just down the road from me. It cost about what I'd spend each month on cigarettes, so it was a meaningful investment. Payback would be very quick as well. I was open to all suggestions, I really wanted this to work.

By 6:00pm on the day of that clinic I had become a non-smoker. I had no desire to smoke. I had no cravings. I have not looked back in nearly a decade, and I had been a dedicated smoker, totally hooked. In those few short hours on that January day, in a Holiday Inn conference room in Milton Keynes, I accepted that smoking was no longer for me, that I had been wrong about it all the time. One by one, the so-called advantages of smoking had been dismantled before my very eyes. We spent little time on the obvious harms etc. We didn't need that; we ignored it, anyway! Instead, each and every one of the 'advantages' was taken apart, until there was nothing. Add in some other stuff, and I knew smoking wasn't for me, ever again.

Fast-forward four years, and now it was time to quit drinking. By then I'd tried a long stint at AA and knew what being sober for a long time felt like. It's good. But still I was in a position where it wasn't sticking, was only ever temporary, and on returning to drinking I was getting worse. It's simply the way it goes. We just get worse and worse. There are no periods over which an addiction lessens, an addiction only ever gets stronger over time, and mine was following this classic pattern.

It didn't take long to search out an Allen Carr Easyway® to Stop Drinking clinic. It was the obvious next choice, as AA wasn't my bag. The other thing to commend it to me was its absolute, proven, success. I had not touched a cigarette in four years after an Allen Carr workshop, so I knew the method worked. But there were a couple of things I hadn't counted on. There are three BIG differences between smoking and drinking:

1.   Public perception: society accepts drinking, but frowns upon smoking.

2. If you say you are quitting smoking, everyone understands why and supports you. With drinking, everyone assumes you have a problem or can cut down. Stopping altogether is weird!
3. Many drinks taste fantastic. Smoke does not!

So I went into the Allen Carr clinic, said hello to the other people in the reception area, and waited for our instructor for the day. There was a little chatter; we were all a bit nervous, I guess, and had never met one another. A common question came bubbling up: 'Do you think it will work?' We were generally positive, and I offered up that the smoking session had worked for me, so I was feeling confident.

Through we went to our 'treatment room' for the day and immersed ourselves in the workshop. Our instructor was fantastic. He himself had been a massive drinker and found sobriety through this very method. He'd even met Allen Carr. He was the real deal, so we were in the best possible hands for this journey.

And so the day progressed, gradually taking apart all the fallacies and lies that surround alcohol. The approach that had worked so well for me before was familiar and made sense. I got it, absolutely, and the interactions in the workshop were cementing this for me. Drinking really didn't make sense. I truly got it.

Around five or six hours in, we were approaching the end of the session and had a short meditation, same as before at the smoking session. This felt great, and set me up for the journey home. Driving home I felt calm, really positive, similar to how I had felt after the smoking clinic. I didn't feel any strong urges or have any pent-up feelings or frustrations. I was generally chilled.

But something wasn't right inside me, and I couldn't put my finger on it at the time. There was some little worm of a niggling doubt in my mind, and I could sense its presence all the time. And this niggling doubt had a name: it was called 'flavour' and it goes like this:

- A fruit cider tastes great – smoke from a Marlboro tastes foul.
- A pina colada tastes great – smoke from a B&H tastes foul.
- A glass of port tastes great (especially with a good Stilton!) – smoke from a Camel tastes foul.

I guess you get the drift. One of the cornerstones of the argument to quit drinking is that alcohol tastes foul. On its own, yes; but we don't drink it neat. It forms a small part of the drink, and the drink tastes good. The alcohol gives the effect and its carrier tastes good. But when it comes to nicotine, we take that in through its carrier of smoke, and that tastes foul. So, making the same argument for quitting drinking as for quitting smoking, that it tastes revolting is, to me at least, flawed. This was the worm that got into my head. It grew and grew, and soon enough I was drinking again.

For a couple of years I thought that Allen Carr had got it wrong, and it wasn't until after I had successfully quit that I realised the truth. I was being a purist. To me, I needed the whole of it to work. I had needed a one-stop shop. AA hadn't provided me with that. Allen Carr had also not done so. I had spotted some small pieces in each of these that didn't work for me, and dismissed them totally. Maybe I was looking for an excuse to go back to drinking?

If I had just accepted that the taste bit didn't work for me, that I should simply put that to one side and consider the rest, then it pretty much works. The same with AA. If I'd have said 80% is good enough, I can fill the other 20% with other methods, then I'd maybe have been able to quit sooner. But I needed to go on that journey and come out the other side. What I suggest to you is that you use my hindsight as your foresight.

Eventually, I pieced together my quit from different sources. Allen Carr's Easyway® was a part of it. Not all of it worked for me, but enough of it did to make a huge difference. Add AA into the mix and a few morsels from elsewhere, and I had my quit recipe.

It would be remiss of me to miss perhaps the biggest morsel of all in the anti-addiction armoury:

Willpower.

And ask the question: Is it all it's cracked up to be?

Willpower and the unwinnable battle

Before we embark upon a detailed look at the various facets of willpower, it is worth making sure we are all clear what it is. For this a simple definition will suffice, and I have chosen one coined by the American Psychological Association:

'[Willpower is] the ability to resist temptations to meet long-term goals.'

An alternative take would be that willpower is the ability to control oneself and determine one's actions. It is self-control, no more, no less.

So why, then, have I started off with a section entitled 'Willpower and the unwinnable battle', when each of the definitions states that it is an ability, first, to resist and, second, to control? If, as these definitions are to be believed, we have this ability and control, then what's the problem? And why a battle?

The primitive mind, located in the amygdala deep within the brain, has remained pretty much unchanged throughout our evolution. It is there to keep us alive, out of danger and in balance. It works without our getting involved, on an unconscious level.

Located in the pre-frontal cortex, within our bulging foreheads, is our modern, thinking mind. It is a miracle of evolution. It sets us apart from all other creatures, and it's what makes us human. This mind has been borne out of our ability to use our innate intelligence to survive, build shelter, use tools and so on. We now have art, literature, music, language and, sadly, conflict. This conflict may be between different individuals, groups of individuals, or within a single individual.

Conflicts between individuals and groups can lead to arguments, even wars. But as for inner conflict, how does that occur? Why does it happen? Put bluntly, your primitive mind heads off in one direction, whilst your modern mind goes in the other.

This manifests itself in people who know they have to stop drinking being unable to do so. They know it is killing them, that alcohol is a poison, that they have to stop. This is the work of the modern, conscious mind. The primitive mind, however, senses something is wrong when its now regular supply of alcohol (which the body has become reliant on to run normally) is cut. It screams out that to survive we need to drink, and we get that feeling called a craving – needing something so much that it hurts, an uncontrollable and irrational desire.

And so the battle commences – ancient against modern – our two minds against one another, in the same brain. It's enough to give me a headache just thinking about it. Our minds are full of chatter all the time as it is; now it's going to be argumentative on top of that! To all intents and purposes, we have a civil war going on in there.

It is into this arena that the weapon of choice, willpower, is introduced. This weapon comes from the modern, logical mind at the conscious level. We are absolutely aware of it, we all have it, and we have all used it. We may want to lie in bed in the morning, but drag ourselves out; that's using willpower. We may not want to revise tonight for an exam, but we do: again, willpower. The common theme is that we use it to help us do something we don't want to do or, in the case of quitting drinking, trying NOT to do something we want to. Thus, we are going against our deepest desires.

So why is there a problem? If we have it, understand it and use it regularly, then why is there an issue? According to WebMD, there are five surprising facts about willpower that may help to explain this, and these are as follows.

1. Willpower is like a piggybank.

You can't take more out of a piggybank than there is in it, can you? A child will save his pennies, putting them away day by day. There are no more pennies in there than he has popped through the slot in the piggy's back. Using those pennies needs budgeting. Likewise, we only have a certain amount of willpower in us each day, and we need to budget that as well. Like the pennies, when it's gone, its's gone. The problem is, our primitive mind will still demand a drink, by craving, even after all our willpower has been used up. With our weapon of choice fully depleted, we are in trouble and we have a drink.

2. Willpower is like a muscle.

To make a muscle stronger, we train. We may run or go to the gym, but we push it to and just beyond its limits. Over time the muscle will grow, get stronger. We all understand this. With willpower the same is true. If you use it regularly and push it a little, it will get stronger, last longer. This is great news, and will really help. Willpower also has another characteristic it shares with muscles: it needs to rest between workouts. A muscle gets physically stronger in the rest periods. It is then that it repairs itself, grows stronger fibres. It gets stronger when it is *not* being used, not when it is being used. Willpower works the same; it, too, needs to rest.

And it's when we're resting that we are vulnerable. We can't call upon our willpower at this time; our defence mechanism is out of action. When a desire to drink comes whilst willpower is at rest, we have nothing to counter it.

3. Willpower is impacted by our emotions.

In a good mood, we have more of it! But it's when we are down that we need it, and that's when it's hardest to access. Similarly, if we have been doing taxing work, using our brains rather than our brawn, willpower is difficult to conjure up; we are wiped out. Looking at our habits, this is when we would have been most likely to reach for a drink, at the end of a taxing day. This is also when our willpower is at its most elusive.

4. Willpower comes and goes.

Unfortunately, willpower seems to have a mind of its own. It comes and goes, and really can't be relied upon. We all have those Can't be Arsed (CBA) days, when our enthusiasm for doing pretty much anything just leaves us, don't we? When a craving hits at this time, we'll drink. Our willpower has seemingly abandoned us. Our conscious mind will know this, but be able to do nothing about it. It can't use something that is simply not there. Again, we are totally defenceless.

So, please don't rely on willpower alone for your quit. You will need other strategies. Similarly, using it as a backup for other methods (we've all seen the 'requires willpower' wording on nicotine patches) isn't a guarantee of success. It's unreliable, and often abandons us just when we need it most!

5.   *Willpower is a renewable resource.*

Ending on a high note, we can recharge our batteries, replenish our willpower. The best way is to rest it and not overuse it. Each night, as we sleep, it's as if we are plugged into a willpower charger. When we wake, we have our full five bars, so don't worry if you are depleted at bedtime; it's all going to come back to help you face the new day

As for willpower being a part of the unwinnable battle, I hope you can see that, in a scene playing out in our own heads, as soon as we drop our defence or it runs out or it's on charge, then we have a problem. The enemy, that craving, that illogical desire, doesn't rest, doesn't need to recharge itself, it's always on. Willpower will keep it at bay, but it will not turn it off. Until you have turned it off, you will face a never-ending, unwinnable battle.

Even so, without willpower, you'll never get started. It simply needs help! But first, let's find out some more about willpower as understanding it will help us use it to its best.

Train it like a muscle

Having understood that willpower is really nothing more complicated than self-control, it's time to look at how we can improve it, and understand why it fails us from time to time. We have also been introduced to the concept of willpower being like a muscle, in that it can be trained to be stronger. I'd now like to explore this specifically in relation to drinking.

Before starting, we need to consider our quit in two parts. First, we have immediate urges to drink, we have cravings. These are in the here and now, they are intense and usually take place in the early days of our quit. They come and go, and usually hit when specific trigger events occur, such as arriving home after a busy day at work, or on arrival at a football game. Second, we have the long-term quit, where we set out our stall to remain off the booze for ever.

It is in these two scenarios that we have a direct comparison with muscular fitness, and this provides some interesting thoughts, and challenges.

For intense cravings that pass quickly, let us use the analogy of a sprinter. For the long-term quit, a marathon runner. What we all know from these two types of athlete is that they are poles apart. The sprinter is fast, a power unit, able to explode into action for a short period of time. For this, he activates his fast-twitch muscles, which can deliver immediate, high power. The marathon runner is typically slight, but has immense stamina and can keep working for hours. She is an endurance specialist, and for this, uses her slow-twitch muscles which work with less intensity, but can carry on working far longer than the sprinter's fast-twitch muscles.

Anatomy lesson over, what does this mean to you and me in our quest to quit drinking alcohol?

Well, it presents us with a challenge, that's for sure. We need to be both the sprinter, to crush cravings, and a marathoner, to sustain the quit. In athletics, natural ability will determine which you might specialise in, but when we want to quit, we don't have the luxury of specialising. We need to be in both camps. We need the immediate power to combat cravings, and we need stamina to sustain the quit. This is what we agree to when we decide to use willpower as our quitting tool.

And willpower, like the muscles we have, can be trained, exercised and strengthened. We CAN increase our power and our endurance, through careful exercise, by following a planned and structured training regime. We can get generally fitter, and at the same time we will find we are naturally better at one discipline or other. In athletics, we are either a champion sprinter or a champion marathoner. In quitting, we have to be both. That means we need to keep an eye on the long-term goal when fighting an immediate craving and, likewise, deal with cravings as and when they appear throughout our quit.

Over time, cravings do lessen which is good news. The issue is that as we won't have come across them for some time, and we are thus not used to dealing with them; our anti-craving willpower muscle will have become weaker over time. It becomes easier to cave. This is why we see so many quits lasting a reasonable amount of time, only to fall apart. If we don't use a muscle, it weakens. Our willpower no longer exists as it did.

193

At the beginning, we may have strong resolve to quit and be able to fend off the cravings, but our endurance willpower is as yet underdeveloped. It has never had to work hard over an extended period. In the early days of a quit, as in the early days of marathon training, we can't keep going too long before we are worn out. A few days is a long time, a few miles is a long way. There's a lot more training to be done before we are ready for the main event, the final quit. And the amount of training we need will differ from person to person. Just be sure of this – there are no short cuts. You can't enter this race unprepared and expect to succeed. Training for that endurance, in the early days, requires periods of rest and recovery, just as the strength training does (and you'll need to keep that up in the long term) to crush those future cravings. As we have seen before, when we rest our willpower muscles, we become vulnerable.

Using the willpower method to quit is a long-term arrangement. By entering into it you are agreeing to a fight, and it's one that you recognise will continue. You sign up for a marathon, but also need to sprint. This is an incredibly tough challenge for an athlete, and it will be no different for you. However you decide to quit, whichever method or combination of methods you use, you will face challenges. It's important to understand what these might be as you set out.

In a sense, by choosing the willpower method you are acknowledging that there will always be a part of you that wants to drink or, at the very least, there is a part of you that wants to drink NOW. What this means is that you are not wholly convinced that you want to stop. If you are not wholly convinced that you want to stop, we could argue that you actually want to carry on. If that is the case, imagine how much harder it will be to quit using your willpower. It's going to be even harder than training for a marathon without there being a race at the end of it.

So perhaps willpower needs a helping hand? It's going to be hard enough trying to be full both of power and of endurance, but without our hearts in it we are setting ourselves up for failure. Maybe we need to work on our initial commitment before we even bring willpower into the equation? We'll mull this over later, but for now, perhaps consider what type of athlete (quitter) you are, and therefore where you'll need more support (immediate quit or long term). That might help you work out what will work best for you.

And while you are thinking about that, do you really *want* to quit or do you *need* to?

Wants and needs

As we go through our lives, it's in our nature to desire progress. Didn't you want a better job, a bigger car, a nicer house and so on? Do you like to eat at the best restaurants or wear the latest fashions? We like to go first class and we work hard to get there.

These are all things that we want, and although we do not necessarily need them, they fulfil an emotional desire to be satisfied, to be progressing, to be making the most of ourselves. To achieve these goals, we set ourselves targets and plan how we will get there. Then we put in the effort and, as a result, succeed. We apply an amount of willpower to this effort, pushing through the tough times, when it's hard work, or when we face unexpected obstacles along the way. We are able to keep an eye on the prize, and this is enough to keep us going.

Of course, once we have scaled that mountain, we see that there is a new one up ahead. Here, we start the same process all over again, enthused by our previous success and knowledge that we can make it if we try. We know we can satisfy our wants.

When it comes to drinking, or rather quitting, this is also something that we might want. Wherever we are in life, drinking too much will, without doubt, have a negative impact on what we do. It will dull our edges if nothing else. It will, in short, lessen our chances of getting on in life. Nobody sets out with this intention, but many of us end up here at some point. It is here that we start telling ourselves that we should cut down or quit.

As you are reading this, I think it's fair to assume that you would like to do something about your drinking, or maybe help someone else. Wherever you are in your drinking journey, if you are here, you have made a decision that you want to stop drinking and you have made a great first step. You may also have heard that this change will need willpower, and no doubt others have judged how much of it you have. You may even have thought about this yourself. In the past, you will have used willpower to achieve things, to better yourself. You don't believe me? I guess you can ride a bicycle. Chances are you had to learn how to do that, and that you fell off a couple of times in the process. It will have been willpower that got you back in the saddle.

Now, there's an interesting thing here. Once you had learned to ride a bike, using willpower, you didn't need to keep using it to be able to keep riding, did you? Further, using willpower as described in the opening paragraphs about getting on in life, to crash through a tough work assignment and progress your career, you could take breaks and recharge your batteries. Using willpower to quit drinking is somewhat different. You can't switch it off or else you are likely to pick up a drink. Drop your guard and you are vulnerable.

There is a second and even more important thing here. Your life goals are things you want. Striving to something you want is pleasurable, and willpower is a powerful ally when times get tough, although you don't need it as a constant companion. Quitting drinking may seem like something you want, but its bigger than that. It's something you need, for without it you will end up with nothing.

You need to quit to save your life.

It is the biggest need you could ever have. You may want to live a long and healthy life, but if you are going to do that, you need to be alive. As an alcoholic or problem drinker, you need to stop drinking to remain alive. But willpower is a fickle friend and may not be best suited to achieving this basic need, at least not on its own. Not only does it have a habit of vanishing from time to time, but it also weakens when we most need it. If our wants are not met, we may feel disappointed, but it's not game over. We can regroup and try again. When it comes to quitting alcohol, the stakes are higher, and for many this is a matter of life and death, and you absolutely have a need to stop.

But if willpower isn't up to the job, what can we do?

What I'd like to suggest is that we might accept that willpower has its limitations, and consider putting it to one side, completely. That is, remove willpower from our quitting strategy altogether. That's right.

Perhaps we should remove willpower from our quitting strategy.

In doing so:

- We would never have to worry about its running out.
- We would never have to worry about its failure to appear in the first place.
- We would remove a painful internal conflict and stressor.
- We could even use it elsewhere in our lives where it performs a better job!

But, I hear you ask, how can I possibly do that? The answer is super simple. Getting there is, of course, a

198

different matter and contained in the pages of this book. What you have to do is decide, with total conviction and zero doubt, that you are now a non-drinker. In becoming a non-drinker, like you were as a toddler, you won't have a desire to drink. And without a desire to drink, you won't need willpower to keep you from it. That's right:

Without a desire to drink you will not need willpower not to drink.

All that you are reading in this book is in fact designed to allow you to explore and find the right way for you to remove that desire.

Willpower is great for pursuing your wants, such as a work promotion. When it comes to fulfilling a fundamental need such as becoming a non-drinker again, it may not be up to the job, so please don't rely on it.

There is, however, one redeeming feature that it has, and we can take advantage of. We wake, each and every morning, with a full tank of the stuff.

If you haven't had a chance to read Dr Kelly McGonigal's book *The Willpower Instinct*, then I fully recommend, as part of your quest to quit drinking, that you do. It will clarify what we mean by willpower, how it works and how we can harness its power. As well as looking at how we might strengthen it to our advantage, the book also considers its numerous shortcomings.

In her book, Dr McGonigal looks at such topics as why being good gives us permission to be bad, and the limits of 'I won't', so critical to an activity such as quitting. The book equips us all with a thing of great power, knowledge. The knowledge it imparts allows us to understand fully what we are dealing with should we choose willpower as our main or partial tool in our fight against addiction to alcohol.

Much of what I have found out and thought about willpower comes from this book, and much is reflected upon in this section. It is now that I'd like to explore one of the main drawbacks faced by quitters relying on willpower. The drawback I'd like to home in on is that our reserve of willpower runs down during the course of a day.

Like a battery

Much like an electric vehicle that's been plugged in all night, we start the day fully charged, all bars lit; we have a full battery. In our car, we know that the battery will allow us to travel, say, 200 miles before it goes flat and we simply grind to a halt. That won't happen, though, as we have gauges to tell us when the battery is running low, so we can plug in and recharge. Further, if we turn on the aircon, stereo, lights and so on, more power is drawn from the battery, and the vehicle's range will fall below 200 miles.

Each morning we wake with a full quota of willpower. Like a car, we use it in every function, navigating our way through choices all day long. For every single situation we face, we have a choice and we need to make decision. Every decision has pros and cons, and weighing all these up takes willpower. We know what we should do, but that's not always what we chose to do, is it? We may be on a diet and have a stick of celery rather than a biscuit. Even then, you will have use some of your willpower in making the decision, whatever the outcome. You will have agonised over it, even the smallest amount, burning through your reserves of willpower. Throughout the day, we all use willpower, and often we don't even know it.

Unlike our car, we don't have a warning light as our willpower battery runs low, and nor can we plug ourselves in and get a recharge during the day, it doesn't work like that. Much like the car, we have a finite amount of charge on board. The trouble is, when ours runs out there's none left for the rest of the day, whereas we plug the car in to fill up. The more decisions we have made in the day, the harder it becomes to make good ones in the evening. The hungry dieter is likely to dial for a pizza at 9:00pm having had a freshly juiced beetroot and kale drink at lunchtime. The alcoholic, trying to quit, will pour wine. There is no defence. Our willpower has been exhausted.

The thing with willpower is that, whatever you use it on, the overall amount goes down. There is no separate battery for quitting drink, staying with your diet or any other goal. Just like the car, whose electricity is used by all sorts of different devices, so our willpower is used by all sorts of activities and decisions. And for the person wanting to quit booze, that is doubly troublesome.

So many times, we have woken and made the 'never again' promise to ourselves and others. In the morning, full of willpower, and regret, our resolve is strong, and this is a reasonable commitment. As we go through the day, two things happen:

- We start feeling better, so maybe last night wasn't so bad after all.
- We use our reserves of willpower on all different activities during the day.

201

Come the evening, after a hard day at work or wherever, we start to think about a drink. Initially we pull up our willpower shield in defence of this, but the shield is weak and full of holes by 8:00pm. It is of little or no use. Soon enough it will disintegrate altogether, at the merest challenge, and we'll drink again. Just when we need it to be at its strongest, it's at its weakest. Willpower will almost inevitably be at a low when we need it at a high. We don't need it at breakfast when we repeatedly vow never to drink again, when we have a full quota of it. As we get to 3:00pm it's running out, and by evening, when the effects of last night have worn off, we feel better again, and our minds turn to an end-of-day drink, our willpower has run dry, and we pour ourselves a drink.

Thus, I would suggest that using willpower to quit drinking is a risky business. You simply don't know how much you have, the rate at which you use it, how much you have left and when it will run out. Imagine setting off on a car journey with that level of uncertainty! I don't think many of us would even start off, would we?

So why do we think it's OK to battle our drinking with willpower? Is it blind faith? Is it conviction? Upon what is this based? Do we understand the potential hazards? Is it not better to be aware of them, prepare for them and understand how we might deal with them? Or do we just put our heads down and go for it, hoping for the best?

Without understanding willpower that, I'm afraid, is precisely what many thousands of people do every single day as they set out to quit drinking. Let's not be one of them. Let us understand willpower. Please, read Dr McGonigal's book; don't just take it from me.

And it's not all bad news for willpower as, with the right training regime, we can make it stronger and last longer. We can send it to bootcamp.

Bootcamp for willpower

Whether you chose to use your willpower as your primary, supporting or supported way of quitting drinking, you'll want to make sure it is as powerful as possible. As I have alluded to earlier, it can be made stronger, just like a muscle, so let's see what type of bootcamp we need to send our willpower to.

Just like in a physical bootcamp, we'll need to make sure our willpower gets a full body workout, leaving nothing to chance and leaving no room to hide. The exercises may be different, but the result will be the same: a more powerful and confident you. I'm actually a personal trainer now, and run bootcamp sessions in a local park. In these I really notice how people who set their minds on a goal will inevitably achieve it. Using that power and confidence you'll be able to face your challenges with that much more certainty, knowing that you are up to dealing with whatever life throws at you.

At this point, I would suggest that joining an actual bootcamp exercise group is also an excellent idea, as it will supercharge your physical wellbeing, as well. Just make sure you check with you doctor first if you have any doubts about starting an exercise routine. (The bootcamp you join will also carry out an assessment – if it doesn't, keep well away!)

Back to it, here are the 'exercises' you'll do in your personal willpower bootcamp:

1. Reward yourself.
2. Believe in yourself.
3. Set clear goals.

4. Have a routine.
5. Build up slowly.
6. Chose the right time to start.
7. Don't beat yourself up.
8. Treat yourself.
9. Get support.
10. Avoid temptation.

So, how do we go about it? Let's get started.

1. Reward yourself.

When it comes to physical training, we can work on strength, for example, or endurance, or different parts of the body, for instance legs or core. Likewise, when it comes to training our willpower, we can concentrate on different types. These will typically be DO something or DO NOT DO something. Whichever we work on, we strengthen our willpower for everything we apply it to. This is great news, and when we have been working it hard, we should reward ourselves. Being kind to yourself is a great way to feel good. After a run I'll have a long hot shower as reward for my tired muscles. Maybe, after a day off the booze, you can think of something to reward yourself with.

2. Believe in yourself.

Well, unless you believe in yourself, I doubt anyone else will. But who cares about them? This is about you so when taking your willpower to bootcamp, leave your doubts behind and approach the session with conviction. Building up a series of little wins will show you that you can succeed, and more and more this will ensure you believe in yourself. Don't restrict yourself to drink-related activities, try anything, as belief can be built on a track record of success, whatever that came in. Get this belief growing and your willpower will expand and strengthen, ready for your quit.

3. Set clear goals.

Be crystal clear with what you want to achieve as you train your willpower. The training is not the same as the main event, but even so you need to know exactly what you want to do/stop doing, so you know you have got there. 100-metre sprinters don't just run 100 metres over and over in their training, nor should you do the same thing all the time. Your goal may be to decorate a room, but you don't just start painting. There is the room to clear, surface preparation to be done and so on. These are the foundations that will ensure your room looks good afterwards. These are the foundations you need to achieve your clear goals. Do not miss this step and, remember, you'll be exercising your willpower even as you do this.

4. Have a routine.

Once you have decided on your goal, you need a plan. A haphazard approach will fail, so you will need to act with discipline. Your personal trainer will take you through a detailed programme of physical exercise to achieve your goals. Likewise, to achieve your goals through your use of willpower you will also need a structured approach, which you will need to follow and not simply pay lip service to. And when you train, you should put your all into it. Sticking to a routine and working hard at it is what will ensure your willpower grows to be its strongest.

5.   Build slowly.

As the saying goes, 'Rome wasn't built in a day', and neither will your willpower suddenly appear overnight as some kind of superpower. Start off building up bit by bit, small chunks at a time. Overdoing it early on and asking too much of it will cause it to fail, and you will become disheartened. Like an athlete who pushes too hard and gets injured, you'll suffer setbacks by trying too hard too early on. Get these little wins in, build on them, and over time they will grow. You'll then be ready for bigger and bigger challenges – eventually the quit itself. Trying to quit the booze without strengthening your willpower first is like entering a race without doing any training. It's not likely to end well. And like training for a race, start slowly and build up.

6.   Choose the right time to start.

A difficult one this, but I'd go along with the old Chinese saying, 'The best time to plant a tree is 20 years ago; the next best time is now.' You don't have to quit drinking now, but you should start strengthening your willpower right away. Alcohol is a poison and will not wait for you; you need to get after it as soon as possible. If you start building your willpower now, you'll be ready for battle that much sooner than you would be if you waited. Don't hesitate. Hit that willpower bootcamp straight away. When it comes to strengthening your willpower, the best time to start is NOW. Choose some simple challenges and off you go, build it up!

7.   Don't beat yourself up.

Something many people do, and I was guilty of it at times, is to be hard on themselves, berating themselves for failing or being weak. Please, do not beat yourself up. You are wasting your energy! Being hard on yourself is no way treat yourself. Remember, quitting is the biggest act of self-love you can administer, so keep it that way. Beatings are never a part of love, nor do they serve any positive purpose. Sometimes I needed to remind myself that I was quitting to get myself a better life, and being hard on myself for the occasional and inevitable failure wasn't going to help me. In fact, this put me in a bad mood, a place where I would feel low, and that's when I would drink.

8.   Treat yourself.

As with rewards, treats are a great way to keep motivated. The difference? A treat is a small indulgence like taking a relaxing coffee break with a chocolate biscuit, whereas a reward is a bigger, less regular thing, gained for sustained effort. A treat helps you keep up that sustained effort. We need help along the way, not just at the end. Treats do that for us. Maybe your treat is a movie night where you can relax, and your reward is a long weekend away. You'll know what works for you. Just don't let the treats take over and do more harm than good!

9.   Get support.

When taking your willpower to bootcamp, you'll really benefit from having others around you. Just like a bootcamp out on the playing fields, where your fellows are supporting and encouraging you, find people to support and encourage you as you grow and develop your willpower. This could be in achieving specific goals at work, where your manager or team can help. Or it could be at home, where maybe you are pushing ahead with a project that needs an element of staying power for you to finish it – perhaps get the family or housemates involved or at least behind you. Any help to keep you going, to help you on your way, should be welcomed, and actively sought. It can do you no harm, just good.

And finally...

10. Avoid temptation.

Specifically, when you are training your willpower so that you will NOT do something, it's generally best to keep away from that thing. Keeping it on show means our minds will focus on it, our attention will be on it. Let's not make things harder for ourselves. We should be doing all we can to make training our willpower a positive experience, as this will be a far more effective approach than any other. Yes, we need discipline, planning and rigour, but we also need to stick with it, and avoiding diversions such as temptations along the way will enable us to do just that.

Emerging from willpower bootcamp, however you do it, you will be in much better shape to take on your quit. Whether using willpower as your main approach or not, strengthening it and treating it well, as we have described above, puts you in a much stronger position for the challenge ahead, that of quitting.

And finally, once you have trained and strengthened your willpower, don't stop going to bootcamp, you're always going to need it for something. Life has a habit of throwing challenges our way. Do you want to be in the best possible position to face them? I know I do!

But perhaps the best advice I can give you? Please, try not to rely on your willpower alone. It's a poor ally, perhaps best illustrated by the following story:

The myth of Sisyphus

According to Greek myth (and Wikipedia), Sisyphus was punished for his 'self-aggrandising craftiness and deceitfulness . . . to roll an immense boulder up a hill only for it to roll down every time it neared the top, repeating this action for eternity.'

This is how I sometimes see quitting drinking, or smoking, using the willpower method. The quit itself is the boulder. You will succeed in your quit when you are able to balance the boulder at the top of the hill. You, pushing the boulder up that hill, use willpower as your strength to do it. Gravity is your addiction, working to pull you back down, working against the boulder resting at the top.

Like Sisyphus, you are unable to attain your quest because of the shape of the boulder, the shape of the hill and gravity. There are too many forces working against you and your own willpower can't overcome them all at once, all the time. Using willpower you, like Sisyphus, are condemned to a lifetime of trying, only to fail. Of course, this is only a myth and some of you WILL beat the odds, but you may be few and far between. Do you think you'll be able to quit through sheer willpower alone? Or maybe you and I will require some kind of assistance, or a different approach altogether.

Approached using this method, the quit is a precarious thing, a round boulder balanced on the top of a rounded hill. Any slight bump and it will come rolling back down, and you'll be back to drinking. You'll then have to start all over again.

Trying willpower again and again this way and expecting a different result would also be defined as insanity; it's not the way to go about things. You are the same person. Alcohol is the same addictive chemical. As these two can't change then something else must. What will have to change is your approach to the quit and how you intend to go about it.

Your willpower, against the pull of addiction, will be a carbon copy of the battle between an irresistible force and an immovable object. Your addiction is irresistible, your willpower is immovable. And herein lies a paradox. The assumption is that both can exist together, but that can't be. A second assumption is that they are in fact two different entities. When it comes to quitting, they both reside in our mind, and we are but one being, with one brain, one entity. The paradox is again flawed. Such is the flaw that one will win out, and time after time after time that will be your addiction winning over willpower.

The reason is simple to understand. Our brains use a lot of energy and as a result are always looking for ways to conserve it. Our brains also have an instinct to keep the peace, to ensure we live in a state of balance. Stopping drinking when addicted or heavily dependent, when our minds and bodies now understand this to be the normal way we operate, puts us off balance. Our use of willpower is essentially an effort to keep us off balance, away from the drink, but from deep within our minds, wanting to restore balance, comes the scream to drink alcohol, which we experience as a craving. If we cave, which we almost certainly will at some point, then the boulder is right back down at the bottom of the hill again. Keeping it at the top of the hill requires massive and sustained effort. This is not for the fainthearted, and failure often leads to more intense drinking afterwards.

Rather than solving the problem, it can make it worse. We've all tried to quit, only to find we end up drinking more when we go back to the booze; it's one of those sad inevitabilities. Instead we decide we'd be better off drinking after all. We also know that's not true, so the battle starts up again. We truly are like Sisyphus, trapped in a never-ending cycle of quit/drink/quit/drink.

Addiction and willpower are not happy bedfellows. As previously suggested, we either need to abandon the willpower method altogether or supplement it with some other type of assistance, an additional quitting strategy. If we can remove willpower altogether, then there will be no battle, and with no battle there is, of course, peace. Approaching our drinking issue whilst at peace is far more likely to produce a positive outcome - a happy quit - than waging war. After all, what we want from our quit is peace in our lives. Drinking alcohol has already brought too much turmoil. We wouldn't be here if it hadn't, so let's step away from aggravation and into calmness. Let's not push the boulder, let's play a different game. Let's take willpower out of the equation, and look to quit another way.

I'd like to suggest that is by way of making a decision. A full-on, all-in, no-questions-asked decision to quit. No ifs, no buts, just pure and simple clarity.

It is the purpose of this book to give you the insights and tools to make that decision, and you are working through them page by page. You will not 'attempt', 'try', 'cut down' or otherwise 'make an effort' to quit. You will stop. Immediately and forever. There will be no looking back. Sisyphus will return to the realms of mythology, never to bother you again.

You will, in the words of Allen Carr, Jason Vale and Annie Grace, be free, and won't need to rely on an unreliable friend in your quit.

That's right, don't rely on it

You know the Japanese bullet train, the Shinkansen, which is always on time, and even stops in line with markers on the platform floor where the doors will be? Well, that can be relied upon. Much like the sun rising in the east and setting in the west, that can be relied upon.

Your willpower? Nope, sadly not. It will, I'm afraid to remind you, abandon you from time to time. You will not be able to maximise your willpower for every moment of every day. Every now and then it will not be there. It will either be exhausted, or will appear to have gone AWOL. Either way, you will not be able to access it. And, as luck would have it, the chances are it will not be there when you need it the most.

Willpower can be a fickle friend and it is also highly influenced by your emotions. When you are feeling happy, on top of the world, full of hope and joy, you'll have plenty of willpower. You'll easily be able to turn down a drink. You'll be confident in refusing a beer because, after all, you already feel great. Your willpower will be in good shape then, when you don't really need it!

Now, picture yourself feeling low, sad, down in the dumps. Getting off the sofa is an effort and even changing the TV channel feels like a trial. You just can't be arsed. What does it matter anyway? Everything is shit, isn't it? Those words, 'Just give me a beer!' said with resignation, will bounce around your head. And your willpower? Nowhere to be seen, it walked out some time ago, and now is the time you need it most.

There when it's of little or no help, absent at your time of need, your willpower is an unreliable partner, one that can't be trusted, one that will let you down time and time again. And even when it is present, you'll be using it on loads of other day-to-day stuff, wearing it out before you might actually need it.

Willpower can be an enormous force for good, but I would caution you against relying on it for anything. It comes and goes and often vanishes when you need it. When it comes to quitting, it may be a useful ally at times, but it should never be the mainstay of your quit. (Well, that's what I think.) Houses built on sand tend to fall down, whilst those on solid, dependable, rock foundations last. Hanging your quit on the strength of your willpower is like building your house on sand, and is as easily blown way. Avoid it if you can!

And remember this: when you are full of negative emotions – anger, hate, despair, depression, loneliness – when you most want to reach out for a drink, to 'make them go away', willpower will be at its hardest to find. When you experience positive emotions – joy, happiness, love, excitement – when you least want a drink, willpower will be there in spades. Willpower behaves contrary to your needs; it's almost like it has a mind of its own!

I'd encourage you to think of occasions when you may have used or wanted willpower, away from the realms of quitting drinking. Consider how you were feeling at the time, and whether you were able to overcome your challenges with ease or found them tough. This will give you a good idea of how your willpower will be when you quit drinking. With that understanding, you'll be able to judge how much you might rely on it as a quitting aid, or whether you might be well advised to look elsewhere. We'll all have different experiences, you'll know your own, and you'll be able to make your own decision based on these.

STARTING OUR OWN JOURNEY

Where to turn

Now that you have decided to end your relationship with alcohol, and even before that, there's a whole lot of advice coming at you from every direction. From friends and family to doctors and even governments, it seems everyone has something to say.

Wherever we go in life, we are surrounded by well-meaning, caring people. On the whole, the vast majority of people are great, supportive of each other and so on. We are social animals and looking after one another is what we do, really well. This care and support is with us throughout our lives. Parents and babies, girlfriends and boyfriends, partners, caring for our elderly, employers and their employees, rarely are we truly alone, and with this support we are often helped through difficult periods of our lives. This is what makes up a true civilisation, how we fit together and support one another.

It is also where I have found that, as a drinker, things can start to go seriously wrong. We are a world of some eight billion people. Each and every one of us is unique, we all have different bodies and minds. We may have a doppelganger somewhere in the world, but it's highly unlikely they'll think the same way! We all therefore have our own world experience and views. We all have different takes on the same subject, given the same information. This is fantastic and amazing, giving us all endless opportunities to learn and grow in each other's company. It also serves up a problem.

The problem it serves up is that each and every one of us also has a unique opinion, and we believe it is right. It is to us at least. How we see the world is how it IS, to us. This will never be exactly the same as what anyone else sees, feels, believes.

How many times in your life has someone said something like this to you?

'If I were you...'

'I wouldn't have done it like that...'

'You should try this...'

'In my opinion you should...'

'You ought to think about...'

'No, that won't work...'

I could go on, but I think you get the drift. The speaker is coming from a place of wanting to help, but is projecting how they see the world on to you. They absolutely want the best for you, want to help, but have no real idea what might be right for you. Only you know that.

The other thing that's a difficulty here is that if you decide to take them up on a suggestion then it was never your idea in the first place. You will not own it, can't truly believe in it and therefore might not work for it hard enough. You may fail, but that's no problem, it was someone else's idea anyway. And here we can get stuck. It may well have been what would work for you, but it could slip through your hands because of how it came to you.

That is why I urge you to find out for yourself, work out what your jigsaw is, find your pieces. Taking a piece from someone else MIGHT work, but it will be from a different puzzle altogether. By all means look into what they suggest, but look deep, understand, see how it fits for you, and only then make it your own. Do not consume it at face value and give it a go. Approaching it that way will probably not work.

The more times this happens, as it did for me, the worse you can feel. We also know that when our mood heads in that direction we are more likely to pick up a drink. Each failed attempt sends us lower. Each failed attempt reduces the number of options left as well, and this got to me. You might get to the point where you feel like saying, 'I've tried everything and nothing works', and giving in altogether.

Maybe it feels that way to you? Do not despair. You can rise from this. It may take a few failed attempts, a few disasters along the way. It may even be that one of the failed options works later on. We change as people, and so a solution we dismissed once before may work now that we are in a different place, emotionally.

Conforming

Wherever we are in life we are expected to conform. As soon as we hit school we are put into uniforms and we are told to wait in line, wash our hands, do this, do that, not this, not that. Soon we are being told to quash our dreams and 'be realistic'. We are asked why we can't 'just grow up', or 'be more like' someone else.

Our freedom is wrung out of us before we even have a chance to express it. And sometimes we rebel against this. We don't like it, we push back, we become problem children. Some of us sneak out and guzzle bottles of Cinzano as young teens, under cover of woodland on a Sunday afternoon. Others may smoke, or try other drugs. Again, we are conforming in rebelling, that's what teens do. As a teenager myself, I pushed the limits, being wholly selfish, but that's the way the teen mind works – it is selfish. Even though we may think we are going against the grain, we are simply doing the same as every teen before us has done, and every teen after us will do.

And then we hit adulthood, which is where I encountered my problems and I think the transition was a defining moment. Physically I became a man, but mentally I was still a child. I still clung on to those rebellious tones of the teen. I was an awkward sod. I just wasn't moving on, growing up. But the thing was, now that I was an adult, I could drink in the open. I could get away with it now. Everyone was drinking and I was no different. Again, I was simply conforming, albeit unconsciously.

Now that I was drinking heavily (and I don't know how many people realised how heavily) and surrounded by drinking adults, I was able to get away with it. The social norm shrouded my problem. I'm sure it shrouds millions of problems around the globe, probably hundreds just in my home town.

But what of conforming? As supporters of a sports team, we wear their colours. As a worker, we may wear a uniform. As a driver, I follow the rules of the road. Whether these rules, written and unwritten, arbitrary or sensible, make any sense or not, we follow them. It's what we do, have always done. Conforming is also easy, it requires no thought and no effort, and that's really attractive. We don't need to justify. After all, that's just the way it is.

And so it is with drinking alcohol as an adult. So ingrained in society is this habit, tradition, whatever you may call it, that it is easier to conform, to drink, than it is not to. Justifying why you are going against the grain is much tougher than going with the flow. And if, like me, you 'enjoy' a drink rather too much, that flow is mighty attractive. Conforming means that questions are not asked of you. Conforming means that you are normal. Conforming means you don't ask yourself questions of what you are doing. You just do.

But alcohol, as an addictive chemical, a potent drug, pushes more, demands more. It's that, alcohol's ability to get us hooked while we think we are safely conforming, which makes it so dangerous. It can creep up on us and when we decide to call it a day, we find we can't. It has sunk its claws into us and won't let us go. Unknown to us, whilst everything seemed OK, alcohol was working its magic, ensuring our addiction. And it's only when we decide to make some kind of a change that we realise there's a problem.

So, when we decide to quit, we are really looking to change two aspects of our lives at once. First and most obviously, we want alcohol out of our lives. Second, we wish to be non-conformist.

And it is on the subject of not conforming that many quitters worry. They are unsure how to go out and not drink, how to tell their friends, how others will react, that they will be seen as unusual, even broken. These all come down to one thing. As people in modern society, we are basically programmed to conform and to expect everyone around us to do so as well. Stepping away and doing something different is often viewed with suspicion; something is not right.

There's certainly a physical side to quitting alcohol, but that generally doesn't last too long. All traces of it are out of our bodies sometime between 24 and 72 hours after our last drink, and we start healing straight away. In extreme cases the physical part is tougher, and medical intervention can be advisable. But then there's also, or more especially, the mental, emotional side. It takes a little longer than one to three days for the difficulties here to be addressed.

Yet still today, adults are expected to drink alcohol. Soft drinks are for children: fact. Or so we accept. And if someone doesn't drink alcohol, the immediate assumption is that they have a drink problem, so guess where the conversation goes? It may go down one of two routes; the 'so your life must have fallen apart' route, or the 'it's going to be so obvious I'm avoiding the subject' route. Neither is comfortable, and it will take time, after quitting, for these to die down. So even when you quit, and for good reason, people will treat you differently.

Getting through this period doesn't take too long, fortunately. Emerging the other side, as a happy non-conformist, non-drinker, is a feeling like no other. You will feel on top of the world, in control and free at last. As a non-conformist, your confidence will soar and you'll find that people will have a deeper respect for you than ever before. You may not have sought validation for your choice to quit, but you'll find it here in spadefuls.

You may have started following the crowd, but you are now fiercely independent of that world, and moving in an altogether better one. A sober one. And as a happy non-conformist, it is with a sense of despair I look at some of the gimmicks, preying on our group mentality, that are used to draw us towards a quit. The one that stands out the most is Dry January. Screaming conformity, it inevitably ends in a BIG DRINK at the beginning of February. So, let's put our drinks down, and explore the phenomenon that is Dry January.

Dry January

As Christmas approaches, January is just around the corner and we all know what that means. New Year, new start. Resolutions. Dry January. Yep, Dry January. We've only just gone through the 'Go Sober for October' charity-fest and here we are again.

Personally, I detest Dry January, and I'd like to have a look at some of the problems I see with it, as viewed from the perspective of the problem drinker, the alcoholic. There are a number of fundamental issues that need to be addressed.

First up, for those of us who want to stop drinking, this looks a great idea from the start. Not much goes on in January, money is tight after Christmas and we've probably been bingeing for a few weeks. Expectations are low to start with. It's not exactly party time in January, is it? So what is the issue? The issue is that January ends. That's right, after midnight on 31st January, we find ourselves in February.

The period of time we are to cut out the booze is limited to 31 days. Once that is done, we have, supposedly, and actually, achieved our goal. We will have survived the alcohol-free desert that is January. The journey is a short one, and it has an end. Once we reach that point, we are free to drink again. Our commitment was for just one month. For people taking part in Dry January, the very fact that it has an end date makes it achievable. Ask most participants to go for longer, two months, six months, a year, and they'll shake their heads and tell you they couldn't do it. But for problem drinkers and alcoholics, those of us who find it even harder than most to put down the drink, that is what we have to do. Permanently. Dry January ends; our quest does not.

Second, consider many of the people who 'do' Dry January. This may not go down well! Let's just say we have a number who are fully paid-up members of the 'look at me' brigade. Throughout the month social media will be flooded with posts and pictures from this lot with such captions as 'I never knew a mocktail could be so good' or 'Sober needn't be boring'. Posed selfies of false jollity abound, 'proving' that they can have fun without getting pissed. Just you wait until 1st February and the booze will be out in force. Which tells us what? Sober may not be boring, but drunk is better? That's the message I get.

Apart from being a self-gratifying ego trip for many, I can't see why they bother. As a drinker, seeing this sort of stuff doesn't help. We must, however, be tolerant, accept the world and its people for what they are, for how they behave, and move on. Being aware of this is important; taking any serious message from it is not.

Then there's the charity Dry January bunch. Yes, these guys really do need to shout about what they are doing so they get the cash in for worthy causes. I'm 100% with these people, and they have totally different motives to stay dry. They don't pretend like the 'look at me' crew. As drinkers trying to quit, these types don't knock us off course.

Perhaps Dry January is a bit of a turn off for you too? It may work and if so, that's fantastic. But, be warned, chances are it may not.

So, as we approach February, Dry January starts to hit the buffers. I remember a while ago, when chatting to some people about this, in mid-January. At the time I was just four months sober. The couple I was talking to were describing how they had booked a table at a really nice local restaurant, their favourite, for the evening of 1st February. We discussed what kinds of food were served, what type of restaurant it was, but almost before we got on to any of that, 'I can't wait to crack open that bottle of champagne' was out. These people were not heavy drinkers, but I could tell that they were itching for a drink. Putting it off for a month made it even more special, would make it taste even better, would somehow amplify its features.

As a drinker, being denied your drink makes it seem even more precious, even more desirable. And once you have it back, you treasure it even more, and it is actually less likely that you will let it go again. So, far from helping people cut down drinking, perhaps Dry January increases the desire for alcohol. Perhaps seeing how much people who were taking part in Dry January drink after that will tell us something. From people I have spoken to, the closer February comes the more excited they become about having a drink, and that's enough of a message for me.

And, let's be honest, it's not taken all that seriously, is it? Dry January? Haha!

Dry gin, dry cider, dry white wine, dry martini.

That's the scale of many Dry Januarys, and for those of us wanting to quit this isn't particularly helpful. Again, society is ramming home the message that drinking is great. After all, who would want a sober January when there are so many 'dry' alcoholic drinks out there? Surely, it's more fun to have a dry gin style of Dry January, isn't it? We could even call it Dry Ginuary!

However, for many of us, alcohol is a very serious issue.

Simply put, drinking alcohol kills us. I have seen friends die. Worse, I have seen them dying over an extended period.

There is another reason why Dry January doesn't work, and it's all about something called habit installation. For bringing this to my attention, I need to thank Robin Sharma, his superb book *The 5am Club*, and his research in pulling it together. He made it clear to me, and it goes like this. Simply, one month will never be enough to change our ways; the amount of time it takes to install a new habit is much longer. If we expect to go through Dry January and keep off the beers after that, then we are setting ourselves up for failure. The habit installation period takes around nine weeks, or 66 days. January has just 31; 66 won't fit!

To summarise then, Dry January may seem a great idea, but for the problem drinker and alcoholic it's nothing but trouble. Also, January may be too early. If I'm not fully prepared and committed to my quit and I start too early, I am likely to fail. On the other hand, if I wait until January comes it may be too late; my drinking may have got to a stage further that I ever expected. Perhaps November would have been the time to start. Any delay could, frankly, be deadly. An alcoholic quits at the right time for them. Don't allow a calendar and the media to decide for you, and make sure you prepare properly, that you go into it with your eyes open.

And so, whilst we are in January, it's a good time to take a look at a grand old tradition: making New Year resolutions.

New Year resolutions

Here are a few of the all-time favourites:

- I'll get fit.
- I'll go on a diet.
- I'll read more.
- I'll quit smoking.
- I'll stop drinking.

Promises, promises! The only thing that history tells us is that we won't stick to them. And experience tells us that nobody else will either. They are nothing but empty promises.

Have you, honestly, ever stuck to a New Year's resolution? And I mean stuck to it – like, forever?

Many years ago, like millions of others, I made a solemn commitment that I would quit smoking. I don't recall the year. As midnight came and went, I barely noticed, and a few minutes later, there I was: smoking. By five past midnight I'd already failed. The next morning, hangover in head, I was desperate for a smoke, and of course I had one. After all, nobody else knew I'd failed. I'd said nothing to anyone about quitting.

And why hadn't I told anyone? Well, for starters, I knew I would fail. Actually, I never truly wanted to quit, and so I already knew I would fail. But why would this be? Why is it that before we make a New Year resolution we don't even believe in it ourselves? And what can we do about it?

Let's look at each of these questions and try to unravel some home truths about quitting, and New Year in

228

particular. We'll then look at one way of setting ourselves up for success.

Here goes with the questions.

Why did I not tell anyone?

Without telling anybody, there is no element of risk or ridicule. Put it another way, if I had announced that I would stop smoking at New Year I would have been greeted with one of two responses. First, there would be the well-wishers, keen to see me succeed, even pleased for me. Then there would be the doubters, even the laughers, who could never see that happening in a million years. And let's say I do trip up and start again. I would feel awful letting all the well-wishers down, failing those who supported and believed in me. And as for the doubters, I'd have proved them right. In myself, I would feel a mixture of disappointment and of anger. I'd have failed myself and those that stuck by me, and played straight into the hands of my doubters.

By not telling anyone, each of these difficult situations is avoided, although another deeper truth is surfaced. That deeper truth is that I am looking either to please other people by quitting (my supporters), or trying to prove others wrong in their assertions that I will fail (my doubters). In each, I am looking to quit because of other people, not myself. If I am quitting for other people, I will fail.

Why did I not actually want to quit?

At New Year, we are all expected to make promises, it's all down to peer pressure. There's talk of renewal, fresh starts, a bright future and all that. Potentially, we all look to something we are NOT keen on in our lives and promise to remedy it. Whatever we come up with is likely to be aimed at ridding ourselves of something. Drinking and smoking are almost too obvious, but they are probably the top two. Maybe joining a gym to lose weight is up there too. And eating less chocolate! If we drink, making a New Year resolution is so easy. It's so obvious. And oddly enough, just thinking about it makes us feel better, before we have done anything. When we tell our brain that we are going to do something worthy, it likes it and we get a rush of 'feel good'. This then confirms we have made the right choice.

Deciding to quit makes us feel we are already halfway there.

We are not, of course. Our brains can't actually tell the difference between an imagined event and a real one. They are both experienced with clarity, and this gives us a false sense of security. We start to believe that quitting will be easy because, in our minds, we have already done it.

Further, because of this, we forget that our hearts were never in it in the first place. We trundle up to New Year and will have made no preparations for the quit, for a major life-changing event. We approach it with no real idea as to what we need to do, what might happen. We do this because, actually, we don't want to quit at all. We never really did.

Why make the resolution?

230

If we know we aren't going to go through with it, then why bother? Perhaps it's because it makes other people happy that we are going to improve ourselves, that we don't want to be left out when everyone else is doing it, or perhaps it's something else. We build New Year up into something special, we want to mark it with something, and as a resolution, quitting drinking fits the bill perfectly. So we make the resolution. We make it because it's the done thing. We make it as an external gesture, rather than from and for ourselves.

If our resolution to quit comes from there, rather than a place of deep and personal meaning and commitment, then we are likely to fail. Getting to that deep and personal place has nothing to do with what the date is, unlike the resolution. Putting down the drink for the final time is about so much more. Getting to the point of being ready to do this can't be done by a simple resolution. It's a journey of hard graft, learning, exploring and understanding. That happens whatever the day. In fact, it probably happens less so on New Year's Eve than on any other day – we are all too busy having fun to think that way! New Year is, probably, the one day to avoid when making serious resolutions!

Instead, let's apply logic to the problem, approaching it with cold, hard reason. That way we won't be swayed by mood and opinion, just fact.

The pros and cons of drinking

Let's start by making a list of the pros and cons of drinking.

Sound reasonable? I think so. It also has the weight of the NHS, one of the most respected organisations in the world, behind it. That would suggest to me that this is going to be something that will work. After all, this organisation is there to look after our health, so it should do. With that in mind, let's look at why it's a great idea.

You see, what happens is that we are encouraged to get a piece of paper and draw a line down the middle. On one side of the line we write down all that is GOOD about drinking alcohol, and on the other all that is BAD about drinking it. As we all know, in our heart of hearts, drinking alcohol (particularly if we have reached the point of drawing up this list with a view to quitting) is, undeniably, bad for us. The list will prove that.

As we draw up the list of pros and cons, what we will see is that those items in favour of drinking alcohol will be outnumbered by those that count against it. Further, those that count against will also be much more powerful, much weightier.

Cancer trumps a good night out.
Liver failure beats a toast at a wedding.

You see, it's inevitable that the BAD will outweigh the GOOD, in number as well as in gravity. As the imaginary scales will tip, we will be able to see, in our own hand, the incontrovertible evidence that drinking does more harm than good.

Yippee! We now know exactly what we knew before. No more and no less. Drinking takes away more than it gives. It costs us more than we earn. It damages and destroys more than it builds. Therefore, the sensible and logical thing to do is to stop drinking. Anyone in their right mind can see that. It is so obvious that even a three-year-old would be able to work it out.

And there's the problem. It is the sensible and logical thing to quit.

However, there is nothing that makes sense or is logical about drinking. We don't drink that way. We drink emotionally, with our hearts and souls and not our minds. We drink because alcohol is a chemically addictive substance that messes with our judgement, all our senses. It defies logic, so any attempt to deal with it using logic, a balanced list, is doomed.

Let us take one observation about alcohol, and look at it a little more deeply. It is something true, it is something that alcohol does, and therefore it needs to be put on the list:

Alcohol makes me feel disconnected from the world.

From the viewpoint of logic, this is a bad thing. We need to be in touch with our surroundings, able to sense danger and threats, opportunities and choices, in order to navigate our way through life. Being out of touch with the world makes us vulnerable. It reduces our defences. We are in a weaker position than we would be without having taken a drink. For a living being this is a very stupid thing to do, as it can lead to injury or even worse.

However, this disconnection from the world is precisely why many people DO drink. A bad day at the office, a failing relationship, anxiety and stress can all be washed away (albeit temporarily) by a generous amount of drink. As we drink, we care less, our worries and stresses become nothing. We unplug and switch off. Whilst we are drinking, it's as if all that pressure and noise is gone. We can feel relaxed again, our problems magically shrink to almost nothing. We forget.

We drink, in this situation, for precisely the reason why alcohol is bad for us.

So, we should immediately put this assertion that 'alcohol makes me feel disconnected from the world' in the BAD column. But NO! I hear you cry, it needs to go in the GOOD column, because it makes me feel better, relaxes me and helps me get through a tough time.

Like so many things about alcohol, it's not all that simple. Good and bad get confused. Logic fails and the list simply makes the problem worse. It makes it worse by making us focus on it, on detailing all that is bad about it. We know all this stuff, we are constantly reminded of it, mainly from within. We know we are not helping ourselves, we know we shouldn't be sending ourselves to an early grave, we know drinking harms those around us.

But writing all this down in the table of pros and cons can make us feel low. Writing such a list often has the opposite effect it is designed to have. Writing it causes a great degree of stress, of fear, of sadness even. Oddly enough, it is precisely these emotions that many of us drink to cope with, or avoid.

The logic of making a list, with the aim of providing evidence, in order to show us we need to stop, is an admirable enough suggestion. And yet, by its nature, and that of alcohol itself, it is invariably doomed to failure. For some, it may even make the problem worse.

Don't get me wrong, there may be people who will benefit from this exercise. I just know I didn't, and this is a personal account.

Now that we have considered one tool that we are encouraged to use to help us quit drinking, and seen how it stands up to deeper scrutiny, let's look at another. It is equally common, used by literally millions every year, multiple times per year. It is also endorsed and promoted by the NHS, quitting services of all sorts, and understood by all. And it is this...

Setting a quit date

Again, this one comes from the NHS, amongst other sources, and it's one that I have always struggled with.

The concept is simple. Pick a date in the future when you will have your last drink and from that point onwards you will be sober. OK so far?

So to setting the date, which do I choose? For instance, today is Thursday 29th November 2020. And today I need to set a date on which I will quit drinking. Alongside the suggestion of setting a quit date, there are some handy hints that we are presented with, such as avoiding days when there may be excess stress or other hindering factors involved. Basically, we are told to choose an 'easy' day. This makes absolute sense. Why would we want to make this any harder on ourselves? I'll return to that.

Here goes then. With my calendar in front of me I get to pick a date. Any date.

Tomorrow is Friday, so that's a no for obvious reasons. One, it's too soon, and two, it's Friday, isn't it! As for Saturday, I'll be off to watch the rugby with my friends, so the beers will be flowing. Best avoid that stress! The week ahead is a tough one at work; I'm not sure I need to add to that with not being able to unwind with a glass of wine in the evening. Oh hell, there's a Christmas party next weekend as well. Christmas, December? Who the hell quits then? OK, so New Year? Well, that's never worked before, so that's a stupid idea. How about... 15th January? OK, that's it.

Thus, I draw a big red circle around 15th January. The day I will quit. The day my life will change for the better.

Immediately, and I've done this and felt it before, my body feels better, more relaxed. My mind breathes a sigh of relief. So far as everything is concerned, I have made the decision to quit, and I know when that will be.

Further, my relief is amplified by the knowledge that I don't have to think about the subject for over a month. After all, a commitment is a commitment, so why should I worry? It's not too far in the future, nor is it too close to today. In fact, it's a perfect date. My sense of achievement and satisfaction is great. And even better, I can have a drink and no longer worry about it, as these days will soon be in the past.

Let's now move forwards in time. We have had a fun, and probably messy, holiday season. Our bodies are tired from too much booze but that's fine; we quit soon. It's now 3rd January. Still nearly two weeks until quit date. Looking at the calendar that's still a fair way off. That's good. The days tick past; 15th January gets closer. We carry on drinking. It's now just a week away!

As the date approaches, something starts building within us. Fear, stress, anxiety. I know I became more and more tense as 'The Day' approached, each and every time. I started thinking that this was it, this is the last 'Monday' I'll ever drink. This is my last ever 'weekend drink', my last ever pint in a pub, my last ever red wine with a roast dinner. To be honest, I started panicking. I had no idea what the future held. I had set a date.

But setting a date doesn't make a quit. All it entailed was putting a ring round a day on the calendar, and thinking,

Aren't I a good boy? I've decided to quit and look, that's when it will be.

237

Further than that, I'd made no preparations. That date was soon forgotten until it was imminent. Then it was scary. I'd never have chosen a date so soon if I knew what it would do to me! And then it came.

My final day of drinking. Down in the dumps, sad, nursing a bottle of wine. My last bottle. It was precious to me. And then came the anger, which I somehow managed to hide. As I was pouring a glass my wife walked into the kitchen, and says, 'Oh, that's a good idea. Could you pour me one, too?'

This was my last bottle. Ever. It was all mine, and I was intent on enjoying every last drop. But now I wasn't even going to be able to do that. Of course, I poured her a glass, with 'pleasure', through gritted teeth and volcanic anger.

Of course, I had done nothing to prepare for this quit. All I had done was circle a date. I had read nothing, talked to nobody, set no safety nets in place, brought in no reinforcements, and had no defences in place to deal with cravings or anything like that. I was totally at the mercy of what came my way.

Naturally, I was drinking within a couple of days. And it was fine. I hadn't told anyone; of course not – how would I look if it didn't work?! That circle on the calendar – it was in my diary, not the one on the kitchen wall that everyone can see and ask, 'What's happening on 15th January?' It was private, my own little secret. Looking back, I know why I hadn't said anything to anyone, and it was twofold. First, telling someone you will quit is hard, and even a bit weird if you say you'll be doing it, but not for another five weeks! In that case, best not say anything. Second, I didn't tell anyone because I KNEW that I wasn't going to stop. It was all a show put on for myself, in myself, and nobody else was invited. I could feel all warm and comfortable inside, in this little lie that nobody knew existed.

I had, however, done what was suggested. I'd picked a date, one that should have no stress around it, and decided to quit that day. It was just that, picking a date made me feel good, proud even. It gave me a boost. It even gave me permission to drink, and that was a bonus. But it didn't mean anything. It was a hollow promise, but as I didn't need to fulfil it until sometime in the future that was OK. I could even get myself ready for it in the meantime. There was always time for that. But I knew I'd never get round to it. My heart was never in it from the start, it was all a scam. I was cheating myself.

So I had broken the quit; the encircled date had been thrown away. Now that I had crossed the line, it was only going to be easier to cross it again. And once a rule has been broken, it's well known that we find it easier to break it again, and indeed easier to break others, even unrelated ones. All that I had done was make it harder to quit in the future. In every way, setting that date, following that advice, had made things worse, not better.

I'd tried this method a number of times. Each time I approached it in the same way. I expected the outcome to be different every time. Of course, it never was, and could never be. I still set out in hope, and always ended up in disappointment.

One day, the quit would come and it did. For me, it didn't involve a quit date. It involved a lot of hard work, hard research, hard reading and, in the end, a couple of days of hard drinking!

239

Maybe, if I'd actually wanted to quit, setting a date would have helped. But then again, if I'd really wanted to quit, then an arbitrary date would have been the last thing on my mind. The quit would have started there and then. And eventually, when the time was right for me, that's exactly what happened.

And now, if I may, I'll return to the idea, given above, that we should choose an 'easy' quit date. The idea behind this is that, by choosing such a date, we won't get worried about anything, our minds will be relaxed and quitting thus comes easier. I understand. But I also have a fundamental problem with this and as soon as I read it, I saw it. We are encouraged to choose an 'easy' date, because in the very next sentence we are being told that quitting will be hard. As soon as we choose the 'easy' date, even if we're nowhere near it yet, our minds are immediately thinking, 'it's going to be a hard day, that one,' and we start, whether we notice it or not, worrying, stressing, panicking even.

Sadly, when new worry, stress or panic arrives, us drinkers tend to drink more.

The very advice that is there to help us quit drinking and, on the face of it, makes perfect sense, is causing the exact opposite to happen.

In fact, once we have chosen that 'easy' date, it becomes the hardest date there is.

That's one for you to ponder...

Talking of 'days', how about we approach our quit, rather than as an event, but bit by bit, and take it one day at a time? That might be something worth considering.

Take it one day at a time

This is one of those pieces of advice when quitting drinking that I find really useful, and used to find really annoying.

Let's get rid of the annoying bit first. Like a child, I would state something along the lines of 'Well, there is only ever one day at a time. What a stupid concept. How else does time move?' or 'If I take it one day at a time, it means I have to keep starting my quit every day.' Well, I've now learned that if that's what it takes, then do it! I was contrary, deliberately so, perhaps trying to make a point and yes, it was childish and ultimately not very helpful. So let's move on from there, into a more fertile discussion. It's important to recognise what happened, and to understand what I can now leave behind.

Perhaps one of the biggest problems many, if not all of us, face is the concept of not drinking again. By this I mean *never* again. Not just for a few days here and there, or maybe having a month's break from it, but I mean living the rest of our lives and never drinking another alcoholic drink, ever.

Is that something you find to be a bit of a problem to get your head around? Well, let's consider the 'rest of our lives' scenario here. What we mean is that, from the moment we have taken that last sip of wine, beer or whatever, and until we breathe our last, we will never again consume an alcoholic drink. For many of us this can be a worrying, if not frightening prospect. First, we don't know how long that will be, but perhaps more importantly, pretty much every one of us pushes our own mortality away as far into the future as possible. This can make the task seem even more

241

daunting, as the 'rest of our lives' becomes longer and longer.

On deciding to quit and agreeing that it will be 'never again', we make an enormous commitment to ourselves. It is also a commitment that we don't understand. We don't know its size, its duration or its direction. And yet we commit to it. This is brave, and we also know that if we don't change what we do, things will end badly.

As we start our lifetime quit, it soon becomes clear to us that this is a bigger task than we have ever encountered. It is a forever thing. Just the idea of forever can make us nervous. There's a real danger that we will start to play our lives in fast-forward. For example, we'll think ahead to a party, a wedding, Christmas or New Year with friends. These may be weeks and months away, but our minds will spin up questions about how we will cope without a drink. How can we bring in the New Year without a toast? A dry wedding? The annual pub crawl with old work friends without drinking? Often, we can't imagine these things.

Looking forward like this never helps. We may become stressed, anxious, nervous, and even decide to avoid some situations altogether if they involve drink. But we don't quit to remove ourselves from society, we quit to get better. In many ways we'll be better company as we won't be the pissed bore again! We'll not cry and tell people we barely know, 'I love you, man.' Oh, the shame!

This approach also makes the task ahead of us seem huge. We pile situation on situation and soon it all looks overwhelming. There's just so much to get through, and we need to get through it year after year after year. It's the thought that we can't handle it that will send us back to the drink. It's hardly surprising, and with a mountain like that to climb, I think most of us would rather stay at base camp, and have a drink to forget about it all. To push it away as something far too big to deal with.

Looking at the concept of quitting as being a forever thing, a 'rest of my life' change, can be daunting and too much to handle. Instead, there is another way. And rather than looking at the rest of our lives laid out in front of us, we can look at it as simply being a series of days. We can look at taking life on, the quit on, one day at a time.

Approaching our quit one day at a time provides us with two very big advantages. First, by concentrating only on the present day, we don't get tangled up in worrying about the future, about how we will be at events in six months' time. Today, now, is what matters.

Second, a single day is a relatively short period of time. In the early days of quitting, it may not seem so, but it is! This means that you only have a few hours to get through at any one time. You can't live more than one day at a time; it doesn't work like that. Time exists to stop everything happening at once. It allows you to tackle everything piece by piece, rather than all in one hit. For your quit, this means that you can take it in your stride. You only need expend your energy on it in the here and now.

With this approach you won't get exhausted, and even better, you can measure progress. A day, two days, a week, a month and so on, you'll build your quit. Successful day after successful day. I know I counted at the start. Doing so can give you a real sense of achievement, something to be proud of. This, rather than worrying about the future, can give you a great boost and help advance the quit.

Taking it one day at a time is taking it as life unfolds, unhurried, calm, measured and stress free. All these factors reduce our risk of taking a drink and, as time passes, these new days become more and more the way we live our lives. Sober days are what we live, we become used to them. I now love them.

There is one other factor that I think needs to be brought up here, and it's one that bothered me for some time. What I was struggling with on the 'one day at a time' thing was that I couldn't see when we could state that we were free of alcohol, that we had succeeded in quitting altogether. All we can say is that we have any number of days/weeks/years behind us and that we are not drinking now. I needed to know that I was free of alcohol forever, and 'one day at a time' didn't answer that. I felt that I'd never know if I had succeeded.

Now that I'm around a further nine months down the line from when those thoughts hit me, I can look back and see that that's all they were, thoughts. They didn't cause me to drink, and now I can leave them in the past. I simply do not know what tomorrow will bring. I am learning to live in the sobriety of today, and allowing tomorrow to take care of itself. Quite simply, the more sober todays I have, the less and less likely it is that I will drink tomorrow.

Do I really need to care whether the rest of my life will be free of alcohol? Or do I just need to concern myself with the here and now? I think the latter. One of the reasons this makes sense to me now is that, having become sober again, I want to enjoy all that each day brings. I want to experience the joy of living, make the most of this precious life, and I can only do that by living in the moment. Wondering if I might have a beer tomorrow, or at any time in the future, isn't going to enhance my today, so I no longer wonder. I don't need to think about it. This, to me, is the sign of a successful quit.

'I will never drink again for the rest of my life, however long that may be and whatever happens along the way' is one heck of a statement to make. Perhaps it's too big.

'I'll not drink today' is manageable.

And as we are only alive 'now', then not drinking 'now' means we have succeeded in quitting. There is no other time, so perhaps taking it one day at a time is the right approach, after all.

But what do we tell others around us? A further piece of advice we are often given is that we should let them know what we are doing. I wonder.

Tell people you are quitting

A few years ago I was reading a book entitled *Influence* by Robert Cialdini. In it he was saying that one of the best ways to ensure something was done, to influence an outcome, was through commitment and consistency. Commitment would potentially take the form of making a public announcement; the consistency would be carrying it out. By making the intent public, there would be a greater chance of it happening. What would be the driver if there was no comeback?

And so we are faced with a choice. To tell or not to tell. Each has its pros and cons, and in the end it is entirely up to you. What you think will help you the most. We'll spend a little time on each.

Telling other people – the advantages

Let's look at how that might help your quit. Before you even tell anyone, you'll first need to decide who you tell. Making this commitment to your husband or wife may be easier than saying something to your boss or your mates in the pub. Some people you know will be supportive, others not so. As I don't know them, you'll have to make that call yourselves, and tell only those you think will help you most, or even just a selection of them.

Having made the choice, and having told them, your life is immediately different from how it was before. You now have a support network of trusted, supportive people around you. They say that a problem shared is a problem halved, so you should feel a huge weight lifted from your shoulders. You can certainly never take back what you have said, and these people will forever know of your struggles with alcohol. This is why you need to choose carefully.

With your commitment made, you now have not only yourself to succeed for, but you also want to ensure you don't let other people down. This can help in that teamwork often gets better results than individual effort. Almost always a team is greater than the sum of its players. Making use of this universal constant can really make a difference to your quit. Your strength comes from everyone else, as well as yourself; you are not alone. As you get deeper and deeper into your quit and those you have told see this, their encouragement should also increase, and you'll get a lift from that. Ultimately, it is always your quit, for you, but having a few good supporters is always handy.

However, there is another side to this coin.

Telling other people – the disadvantages

Again, you'll have to go through the decision of who to tell and then share your plan with them. The thing is, however well we think we know people, there are bits we'll never know. They don't know everything about you, so why should you about them?

There are two things I'd like you to consider here, and let you work out what is best for yourself. One relates to time, the short-term and the long-term, and how those people you have told may react, and thus impact on you. The other, to pressure.

Time first. People may react in ways you do not expect. Some will deny you have a problem (perhaps they like you drinking as it makes their drinking habit seem less of an issue!); others may question your ability to keep off it, thus knocking your confidence before you've even started. These are the early issues you could face. Later on, as time has passed, an altogether different beast will rear its ugly head amongst even those who support you most. This is the thought that we all have after some time, the 'Surely one won't do any harm', or the 'Come on, you've got over that now' thought. It will come, and the more people you have told, the greater the chance of it being said. This can easily knock a quit off course.

Next up, pressure. Telling people you are going to do something is very different from actually doing it. To the brain the act of telling feels like the doing, but it isn't. You will sense an immediate physiological change and feel better for it. This will give you a sense that you have done the right thing in telling someone else, that you have set course in the right direction. But what if you were to fail? What would you tell these people? You may feel you have let them down, or confirmed that you are weak and can't control yourself. Have you just put too much pressure on yourself? If so, what is your usual way of releasing pressure? Having a drink? Maybe you have just made things worse than before.

Perhaps you would have been better off keeping quiet and telling nobody. After all, it is your quit, and nobody else's.

Not telling other people – the advantages

Well, for starters, if you slip up nobody will notice!

Often, other people won't even realise you have a problem, so why advertise it? How much good is it really going to do? If, like me, most of your drinking is or was done behind closed doors (and let's face it, most alcoholic drinking is), then making it public is like airing your dirty laundry. We don't do that! Keeping our quit to ourselves means we have nobody else to please, to answer to, but ourselves. We can't let anyone down; we won't disappoint anybody by failing to keep to a commitment. We own our own problem and can chart our own course through to its resolution.

By telling another person, we also open the floodgates of advice. 'If I were you' and 'Have you tried...?' comes tumbling forth from well-meaning friends and colleagues, most of whom understand nothing whatsoever of what you are going through. This tsunami is avoided if we keep quiet. It is one less thing to worry about, and the less worry we have the less stress we have and the less likely we are to drink.

Perhaps silence is a good thing, although it may not always be the case.

Not telling other people – the disadvantages

So, here we are all by ourselves, trying to quit. We are on our own little island, isolated and cut off from the world. Nobody knows what we are doing. All the time we are battling our demons. We have no backup. We have no allies. We have no support network, and there is no way off the island. By not telling anyone, perhaps we will withdraw into ourselves and make solving our problem even harder. If we break a secret commitment we have made only to ourselves, nobody will notice, as nobody ever knew about it. We may think nobody cares, as we haven't given them a chance to. Imagine how that will make you feel. Do you want that?

No, I don't think keeping it to ourselves is the answer. It's an avoidance tactic. And when it comes to saving our lives, avoidance is a non-starter.

Confrontation, then commitment, then consistency, that's what we need.

Quitting is a commitment. Keeping a quit is all about consistency. It can be a rocky road, so choose your travelling companions carefully!

If you aren't sure who you can tell or not tell, who you will choose as your travelling companions, or what you can and can't say to your friends and family, there is another way. You can confide in total strangers, in a safe place, and have a support network all wrapped up in one package. It can be a heck of a commitment but, for many, it's worth it. It might be worth looking into AA. For me, it needed a bit of a health warning; it can become addictive in itself. However, for millions around the world, AA simply saves lives. For that reason alone, I suggest you try it.

We know the facts

Please don't ram them down our throats.

Take 1:
Them: 'Sir, you do know that drinking can do serious damage to your health, don't you? I mean, if you carry on you could get really very ill, even die?'
Me: 'Oh my word, I really had no idea. I must stop immediately. Thank you so much.

Take 2:
Them: 'Sir, you do know that drinking can do serious damage to your health, don't you? I mean, if you carry on you could get really very ill, even die?'
Me: 'You really think I'm so stupid that I don't know that, you twat? Now fuck off!'

Or, simply put, and by way of an example, people see packets of cigarettes with a notice that "Smoking Kills" and still smoke. Seen often enough, don't we just tune out these messages? They become background noise. Don't you ignore them too?

If any of you were ever smokers, you'll remember National No Smoking Day, which still takes place in March every year. Perhaps you were like me then. I used to smoke far more on that day than any normal day, out of anger and spite at being preached at, lectured and told how to live my life. Gawd, how I hated those self-righteous prigs ramming the bloody stop smoking message down my throat! I quit in the end, but still hate them. But we are here to talk about alcohol and drinking, not nicotine and smoking, although

I'm sure you can guess how I feel about health messages and being 'educated' as to the dangers of drinking.

Let's get this straight, out of the way, in the open. Like every other drinker in the world today (and for quite some years now), I was not born in a cave. I have not been denied access to knowledge, education, science and society as a whole, and I have not been living as a hermit. Like every single other man, woman and child on this planet, I have been a functioning member of society, communicating my way through life. We all have our different ways of navigating from birth to death, but we are all conscious of the world around us.

That's the Mr Angry bit done, so I'll carry on now.

What I am addressing here is the approach some people take in providing advice to drinkers. This advice is dispensed to all drinkers, from those just starting out, to social drinkers, to functioning alcoholics and beyond. It staggers me that this advice is given and yet it is. The advice which goes along the lines of:

Alcohol is a dangerous and addictive drug that ruins lives every year, bringing death and misery to millions, devastating individuals, friends, families, livelihoods, everything. As a result, you shouldn't drink it.

OK, great, that's really helpful. Of course I know all this. I see it every day. I KNOW these things and, yes, they sometimes scare me. I understand that thousands die every day, that innocent people are killed in traffic accidents. I get it, I really do. But banging on about what I already know, ramming the obvious down my throat, filling me with negative thoughts, saddening images and depressing facts is really not going to energise me, fill me full of optimism and a can-do attitude where it comes to quitting.

By concentrating on the bare, unfiltered facts about the harm and danger that drinking brings, all that it is bad for, really makes me want to get away from it all. These thoughts and images are stressful, and many a drinker's default mechanism for dealing with stress is to drink. Maybe bringing these things into the open stirs up memories, revives emotions, or simply puts people's backs up. In all these situations, a drinker will more than likely pick up a drink to drown out the stress and negativity. I know I did.

My suspicion is that those who have promoted the idea that discussing all those things that are bad about drinking, to 'educate' the drinker into stopping, have never been problem drinkers themselves. The drinkers of the world push all these things to the backs of their minds. Far, far back.

Instead, we seek the 'benefits' drinking brings us. Stress relief, boredom relief, escape, oblivion, even laughter, camaraderie, friendship and belonging. Drinkers drink because, in some way or another, logical or not, drinking helps them. Drinking makes life easier to deal with. Drinking keeps the wolves at bay. Drinking is a defence mechanism. Yes, it's a faulty one. Yes, it will eventually fail in these jobs as well. But until that time, for the drinker, drinking is a good thing.

And we do know the downside. But just consider this. If we could stop, get off the train, would we? Could we? Addiction takes away that choice. The exit may be obvious, but it's rather like telling a prisoner to open his cell door, without a key, and walk free. It's the same as telling an alcoholic that drinking is bad for him and expecting him to put the drink down.

We, as drinkers, know the facts. We are part of the world just like everybody else, so we deserve to be treated that way, with respect, understanding, compassion, and not with disdain and incredulity at what others perceive to be weakness and stupidity. Quite simply, concentrating on the negative aspects of the situation is never going to make it better.

Looking back, it is the promise of a better future that we need to focus on. And by removing drink, you allow space for good things to come into your life. The longer you leave it, the bigger the space for more good things.

And that's a promise!

A safe limit?

First up, the advice from the NHS is that we should limit ourselves to 14 units of alcohol per week – that's around six pints of beer or lager, or ten small glasses of low-strength wine. Any more than that will be doing us permanent harm, I guess. Oh, and this should be spread out across the week rather than drunk in one or two sittings.

I know that at my level of drinking I was off the charts! Does anyone else look at these numbers and go, 'Yeah, right – each night more like, and that's before the weekend comes along'? I know you're out there, but don't worry, the NHS gives a pretty decent list of tips to help us cut down. Some may well help you, and I'm going to have a brief look at each in order, giving my immediate and honest reaction to them.

So, working through each of the tips, here we go. Please do take your time to think about each of these before moving on:

> 1.   *Set out how many drinks you will allow yourself next week.*

Picture the scene. You have just decided that, as a heavy drinker, you wish to reduce your alcohol intake. It's pretty much immaterial if you were a lone or a social drinker, but let's stick with considering the lone drinker, much like I was. It's Sunday night and the decision is made. It's time to deal with the drinking problem. I would imagine that you, like me, would have a last few drinks to say goodbye to the old days, with all good intentions set for the coming week.

All is not lost; at least you can have a drink each day. It's not that bad.

Come Monday evening, having been drinking a bottle of wine every night, today's allowance is one small glass. You'll delay having it until as late as possible; the last thing you want is to have had the taste of it at 7:00pm and then be denied any more! Maybe you get through Monday, well done. But that's the future: delay, denial, disappointment. What of Tuesday, Wednesday or, worst of all, Friday night?

By cutting down like this you are still a drinker, but you will put yourself through the mill every night and day from now on in. It's a tall order and it's more than likely you'll throw in the towel after just a few days. After all, who wants a life bereft of pleasure? That's what you might have because, by allowing yourself to carry on drinking, you still hold out that alcohol brings you pleasure. I think it's hard to live a life in denial of pleasure. As such, I have reservations about this as a great tip.

2. *Set a budget to spend on drink next week.*

With budget setting we face three problems.

First, look above. It's very like setting a limit on the number of drinks you allow yourself. We know that's a problem.

Second, what happens when you run out of budget on Tuesday and have the rest of the week and the coming weekend to go before the next injection of cash? It's really quite simple; you revert to paying by contactless card, set up a tab in the bar or simply go to the cash machine. You'll 'borrow' from next week – and anyway, how many people know what your budget is? Did you tell anyone and even if you did, are they counting? You will, I'm sure, obliterate the budget quite early on.

Third, in order to stick to a budget, what can happen is that we will look at value for money. We look for the cheapest 'per unit cost' – high alcohol content, low price. Cider? Cheap vodka? This is a slippery slope, isn't it? I'm sure it's not what is intended, but I can see it happening.

3.   Tell friends and family.

This may seem a great idea, and you'll get great support from many, which might well help you out as you embark on your quest to cut down your drinking. It can really do you no harm, except there are a couple of situations I'd like to point out on this one. Do you really want to tell your friends? Will they judge you? How will they react? How will you remain friends if you can't have a few beers with them? Will they try and convince you otherwise? Maybe, like so many, they'll see it as a temporary measure, and question how long you are on this health kick for. Maybe it would be best to step away from some friendships altogether.

Your family will probably be a greater source of support, but if you go back to the booze, the pain can be harder. The other thing I found with this one is that I broke so many promises by saying I'd cut down, time and time again, only to drink again. If your drinking really is a problem, your family may just want you to stop. They are probably right, so cutting down won't really do it. Remember also, be selfish, quit for yourself and everything else will fall into place. Cutting down may well perpetuate a cycle of broken promises; quitting breaks it for good.

4.   Cut back a little each day.

I must say I've never tried this one, but it interests me. In theory, this is a great way to reduce your alcohol intake, by gradually reducing the amount you drink, day by day. The issue I have is twofold. First up, problem drinking, alcoholic drinking, is characterised by our lacking an off switch. Thus, once a drink has passed our lips, we will continue drinking until we drop, fall asleep, run out of time or run out of money. We will not be able to stop at drink number three if we used to drink four. If we have a broken off switch, it basically means that cutting down is not an option.

The second issue here is that we still hold on to our absolute enjoyment of drinking, and are starving ourselves of this enjoyment. By denying ourselves a pleasure, we are making it even more special, more desirable. Doing this, we are setting ourselves up for a fall in the future. Imagine the feeling of release when you say 'To hell with it – I'm on holiday/it's the weekend/my birthday/any event.' After all, your mind will say, 'I've been so good cutting back bit by bit this week, I can have a few more tonight!' It's as if you've saved up some drinking credits – and you give yourself permission to spend them later on.

Not quite what we are after, encouraging binge drinking, but that's one of the dangers here.

5.   Make it a smaller one
(a 330ml bottle rather than a pint!).

Yeah, right! And if I do, I'll simply have ten halves rather than five pints! Actually, I'll have a half, realise it looks daft, and move on to a pint straight after! Small glass of wine?

Top it up again, will you? I'm not sure who came up with this one, but it's clear to me they've never had a drinking problem. What do you reckon?

6.   Have a lower-strength drink.

That can be a challenge! I drank Green King IPA and Blossom Hill white, mostly. Find me a low-strength beer that's anything like that IPA and I'll give you a medal! And as for 5% wine, it's like water and doesn't taste anything like the wine I enjoy. If you are a spirits drinker, then low-alcohol gin or vodka is an interesting prospect – and anyway, what would be the point? I once tried a herbal 'non-spirit'. Not for me; it was utterly disgusting!

Let's all remember that the reason we are reading this book is that we have a serious drinking issue (or have an interest in the subject at the very least) and will often drink for the effect it has. Over time, many drinkers will want to increase the strength of what they drink. As their bodies become accustomed to it, more and stronger drink is needed to gain the same effect. Looking for a lower-strength drink defeats the whole object of drinking.

It is that objective we need to address, not the strength of drink. If we are drinking to block out our world, then let's make it a better world that we don't need to block out. That way we needn't drink at all. It's about a better future, not a weaker drink.

7.   Drink water between drinks.

I can't argue with this one, it's a great idea and it works. It does keep you more sober and simply means your capacity to drink is reduced. BUT I've found it only really works with a meal – dinner out, for instance, with a specific glass of iced water next to your wine glass. As for trying this whilst watching rugby on a cold winter's afternoon, no thanks, not a chance. Or sitting in a pub garden on a hazy Sunday evening? Ice cold lager, with a water chaser? I'm a drinker, what do you think? Yes, I agree that drinking water between can help, but it's not exactly a long-term solution for an alcoholic. After all, water is for fish to swim in!

8. Have several drink free days each week.

Deny, deny, deny – then binge!

Maybe not the best for me. You may find it works. The real problem I find with this one is that by the time I would get to a drinking day, I know I would immediately ignore the 'units per week' limit and have as many as I fancied, and more. As we know, once we've had a couple, any notion of being told 'that's enough, you know' will go right out of the window. I never did try this technique, but see it being particularly impotent for those who need it most.

In summary, if you want to reduce the amount you drink, cutting down means the following:

1. You want to keep drinking.
2. You see drinking retains some benefits for you.
3. You accept putting yourself through tough times.
4. You accept denying yourself the pleasure of drinking.
5. You will exercise total self-control over your alcohol consumption.
6. You will stop when you hit your self-imposed limit.

If you can't accept all these, then you'll be heading out into a miserable world – and you'll probably carry on drinking just like you did before.

Quitting totally removes all these problems; cutting down makes them worse.

If you drink alcoholically, that is, to a level that is causing you problems in any sphere of your life, it is likely that cutting down isn't going to solve those problems.

But what about the pub?

Well, what about it?

It's not really about the pub though, not the way I look at it. What I mean is that there are certain times and places in our lives that we have tended to end up drinking more and more. Generally these times and places were those that we enjoyed for their own sake when we started out, before alcohol invaded them. I'll suggest three such things, and I'm sure you can think of plenty more for yourselves. Once suggested, we'll watch them develop over time. For me, these three are:

1. Watching live sport.
2. Gigs.
3. Barbeques.

No, not going to the pub (that comes fourth).

Taking each as an example, we'll start with my annual trip to Lord's to watch a day of Test Match cricket. I started going when I was around 12 or 13 years old, and would diligently watch the game, following every ball, not missing a second of the action. A friend's father would drive us there and back, and look after us all day. It was a massive treat and a great day out. Over time, I learned to drive, and would take my own father to these games as he was also a fan. We'd take a picnic, maybe meet some friends there, have a chat and watch some cricket. Again, this would be a great day out, a social event with cricket and company. As time went by, I started having a drink or two during the day, and eventually it ended up being just me and my brother going to the games, each time drinking more and more than the previous year, and watching less and less cricket. I can't

262

even recall who was playing last time I went. That day out had started because of my love of cricket, and it became a drinking day, no more, no less.

Now I no longer drink, would I avoid that situation, that day out? No way. I still love my cricket and a day out there is super special. Why would I deny myself a real pleasure? I could still watch much of the game, catch up with friends, have a meal and not drink. I know I'd remember the day as well, which is always a bonus! That day out had become an annual booze-fest, but my underlying reason for being there, my love of the game, remains, and I can truly enjoy it again.

It's a similar story with gigs, although drinking and gigging went hand in hand from the start. I started off with my first gigs in the early 1980s when you'd get served alcohol at the age of 15 or 16, no problem. I remember venues like Queens Hall in Leeds, Hammersmith Odeon of old, and various university campus halls where bands, big and small would play on long tours. I was into my heavy rock, and beer was part of the scene for me. I'd often come back from the bar with two pints for myself, having necked one at the bar – I didn't want to queue up too often, did I? I'd offer to get drinks for my friends, and grab another at the bar while I was there. All too often I'd end up three sheets to the wind and recall just a wall of sound rather than any actual music that was played! Still, I'd had a good night out – drinking.

Older now and sober, I've been to quite a few gigs since quitting alcohol. In every way they're better than ever. I can see properly, hear properly, don't spend half the time at the bar rather than watching the band, and can drive home, get a decent sleep in and be ready for the next day. I don't need to think about where they are, what day they are on, or even how much they cost, as they'll always be so much cheaper than with the umpteen beers before. Quitting drinking has given me the chance to enjoy gigs more than ever, and get to more of them. That's what I call a win-win situation.

My third drinking issue really came with barbeques, or maybe just meals round at friends and family. I would look forward to these for days, weeks even, as they were a legitimate reason for me to get drunk, very drunk. My wife would always say, 'Now, you're not going to get plastered this time are you?', to which I'd respond, 'No, of course not', and then proceed to get plastered anyway. I've destroyed DJ sets, collapsed into tables of food, been carried back to my room after drinking vodka with a Russian, and made a fool of myself on countless occasions. I'd always get to that ideal level of drunkenness, but be unable to stop drinking more and more. My off switch doesn't work, and the problem with barbeques is that they encourage drinking on arrival, regardless of the time of day. Naturally, I'd be straight into the beers, and it's never questioned. It's ideal territory for a drunk, but also dangerous ground.

It's also ideal territory for a really good catchup with people, a laugh and a joke. Looking around I see that most people have maybe one or two drinks, not eight or ten. Not having a beer in hand is no big deal; nobody actually cares. If anything, people are probably quietly relieved when they see a coke in my hand now! Nowadays I can hold a proper conversation with people, engage with them in an interesting and interested way. That's actually having a good time. Getting pissed in public isn't so great.

So what does this tell us about the pub?

What it tells me is that once we put the drink down, we can rediscover life, what made us happy before, and return to that. Just because I turned what I enjoyed into drinking events doesn't mean that the underlying reason for being there has changed. I still love cricket, I still love live music and I still love the company of friends and family. Now I can enjoy them even more and it's also great to get back in the pub with a fun group of friends, knowing I'm safe, sober, and able to enjoy their company on my own terms, not on those of alcohol.

Disappointment

Before we get to our final, true quit, we will inevitably have failures to deal with, and feel disappointment. Indeed, over the years I have made various attempts at quitting alcohol. I vowed that I would quit when "*x*" happens, and I made many 'never again' promises to myself. I occasionally bought tokens for my wife to show how sorry I was and that I'd never do that again. But because I fundamentally had no idea what I had to do to make a quit a success, I would fail, and drink again.

With no idea and no plan, I was doomed to failure before even starting.

That failure fuelled frustration, anger and disappointment. I had to deal with it over and over again. Each time I attempted a quit I would do the exact same thing expecting a different result. We all know what that means; it's the definition of insanity, and I expected it to work! It never did, and each time I failed I felt even further away from being able to quit.

The problem was compounded by a well-understood fact, phenomenon really, that each time we return to drinking after a quit we tend to drink more than we did beforehand. We all tend to drink more over time (there was a time when we didn't drink at all, so that's got to be true) and this makes for a real dilemma. Trying to quit and failing makes us drink more. So why try? At least it won't get worse. But sadly it does, bit by bit. It's just that quits tend to make the increase move in jumps rather than smoothly over time, and we notice it more. It is these jumps that get to us, disappoint us, and often lead to big gaps between quit attempts.

So what can we do about this, how can we make our journey into the laboratory a productive one? First up, we need a bit of training, we need to learn a little about what we are about to do, maybe find out what people have done in the past. Second, we need to expect to fail a few times. It is said that Thomas Edison tried over 10,000 versions of a light bulb before getting to the one that worked. He also said that he didn't fail 9,999 times, he just found that many ways not to create a light bulb. But I bet he learned a little bit from every one, and that these lessons enabled him to crack it in the end.

I'm not saying that you'll have 10,000 failed quits before you get there, just don't expect miracles. It may take a while, and you may need to find a 'pick and mix' from different techniques and suggestions to get the combination that works for you. You will surely need to show a degree of perseverance in getting to your quit, and you will find that it's a bumpy road ahead.

So long as you keep reading, talking to others, checking out the resources that are available to you, you will be learning, getting closer to what works for you, in your quit.

As a baby, the master craftsman had not yet picked up the tools of his trade. As he grew, he became curious, interested, and eventually took up an apprenticeship. He worked hard and years later he emerged a master. It is said that it takes up to 10,000 hours (that number again!) to master your craft, so don't expect your quit to work from Day 1; that's quite unlikely. Temper your expectations and when you would otherwise feel disheartened or disappointed, learn from it. AA wasn't for me, and nor was Allen Carr's Easyway®. I couldn't get on with a therapist, and some of what Annie Grace says doesn't sit well with me.

267

On their own, these techniques for quitting could be counted as failures and, without each other, for me, they were. However, over time, one attempt or piece of knowledge building on the other, combined with my understanding and maturity in the subject continually developing, they came together and formed a solution for me. When I got to my final and successful quit, all these various pieces and more came together into a coherent whole. I had found my light bulb and it worked.

On the way there, it's not about beating yourself up if certain techniques don't work. Try not to get down if what worked for one person doesn't work for you. You will go through times wondering when you'll get there. Keep going because by persevering, you will succeed. Stopping trying will only ever keep you where you are, and that is a place you don't want to be, I know. Each time you try something, read something, watch something on YouTube about quitting, see a TV documentary, you are building up your knowledge and experience. Keep curious, keep looking, keep digging into the subject. There is no substitute for a solid foundation for your quit. With that, you are setting yourself up for success.

Try and treat your disappointment and frustration as 'OK, next please!' moments and remember, these emotions will teach you something, even if it's what NOT to do – and all these lessons help!

When it comes to quitting, you can never stop learning, so embrace this. Every minute learning is a minute moving away from disappointment, anger, stress and drinking. Be patient, expect the odd failure, but be stubborn in your purpose. I know that having completed a successful quit I have become a stronger, happier and more fulfilled person in every way. Now it's your turn!

But first, let's have a final dip into the world of quitting.

QUITTING FOR GOOD

A drinking career – I needed a career change!

When we hear the word 'career' we tend to think of the world of work, of a progression through the ranks as we grow and become more and more capable. Perhaps ambition springs to mind, a desire to get on and improve one's lot in life. There are plenty of career advisors out there, and many people have career plans and discuss them regularly with their boss or other trusted individuals. Careers build success on success over time, and are the result of having direction and dedication.

I also hear about people's drinking careers, how they have moved from moderate to heavy to dependent drinker. It sounds similar to the progression people make from apprentice to master, where single-minded and focused determination is needed to achieve the highest status.

Is this really how our drinking days are measured? They follow the same pattern of progression; it's almost relentless. We seem to put a lot of time into it, research all the available options, drinks and mixers. In the end we find a specialism and focus on that. Mine was IPA in the pub and white wine at home. At times I even looked and asked myself why, much as I had done when I was a smoker: why do I drink?

The answer made total sense to me at the time. I would say, 'I like it, and I'm good at it', as if this was reason and justification all rolled into one. People who are successful in their careers will tell you they like it, that they are good at it, that it takes effort, but that it doesn't feel like work because they believe in it and love it. Before alcohol took its grip on me, I drank this way, and up to a point I had a successful career. Maybe I never made it to master status, but I was a pretty good journeyman drinker, let's put it that way.

But unlike a working career, alcohol doesn't pay the bills, it doesn't continue to fill us with enthusiasm, it progresses in a downwards direction, and it takes away, rather than enhances our self-esteem. Drinking is more anti-career than career.

When drinking, I was almost delusional about it. I saw it as having some sort of cachet to it, that it was some kind of positive sign that I was someone who could 'handle his drink'. Only I couldn't. Slowly, drinking was dismantling me and all that was around me. As my drinking career blossomed, so every other aspect of my life began to wither.

I needed a career change, and it was high time I made it happen. The change would need to be a 180-degree turnaround, I was heading for a career in sobriety and at the time had no idea how much fun it was going to be. Had I known, or actually believed what I was being told about it, I'd have started out years ago.

Drinkers are strong people

As I suggested in an earlier section, us drinkers are determined, dedicated, resilient and resourceful people. We are strong! Perhaps we should look at these as gifts on our route out of drinking? Maybe these are the very characteristics we need to help us quit:

- Determined: yes, I really, really, will quit, and make it permanent.
- Dedicated: I commit myself fully to this new life.
- Resilient: I will not be deflected.
- Resourceful: I will find whatever works for me, and implement it.

And having done the work, prepared yourself for your quit, which will take all these powers and more, you will get to quit day totally ready for your new life ahead.

Your quit will then be a simple event. It will be marked by putting a glass down, your final glass of wine, beer, whisky or whatever. As you place the glass down, release your grip, and remove your hand for the very last time you will, immediately, start to live in truth. The lies end and the deception is over.

You will be stress free, you will be calm.

In the first days after quitting, you may face a few challenges, but none as tough as any you have faced in the past. Sober, your determination, dedication, resilience and resourcefulness will be turbocharged and, using this power, any cravings or doubts can be obliterated, immediately.

You had high levels of commitment to find a drink when you were still a drinker. Use this same commitment that exists in you against the drink. You already have it in you to stop. Redirect your energies and you will succeed. You may not manage at the first attempt, but you'll never forget what you learned from it, and that knowledge will give you extra strength and experience for the next time. Your determination will get you back for another attempt, and you'll get there.

Whilst drinking, I picked a few people I maybe shouldn't have done as friends, or more accurately, acquaintances, and now that I'm sober they are no longer a part of my life.

Sober, I feel that the people I now connect with do care about me, and I about them. I am actually, and probably for the first time, realising what a friend is. The people I am now spending my time with are those types that have the same sense of fun as me. The more time I spend with these friends I realise that, like me, they too are driven. I feel that I have purpose, a degree of enthusiasm for life that I never did. With this, I am gaining more and more confidence as the days pass. I am putting my hand up to do things, to join in. I am, in short, becoming involved in life. But more than that, I'm becoming involved and interested in other people's lives.

Rather than looking in on myself, which I did so much when I was drinking, I am spending more and more time looking outwards. It is taking time for this to happen and develop, and as it does I am finding myself getting involved in new and exciting ventures.

And in an amazing turn of events, I have recently been presented an award, a Rose of Northamptonshire Award, for 'Dedication to the safety of the community throughout the coronavirus pandemic'. I have been working with a local group of blind and partially sighted people recently, providing socially distanced and online fitness classes, and they wanted to thank me for it! With a drink in my hand, this would never have happened. Getting sober, that brought me to the right crowd.

So, believe me, you may not know what it will be, but good things happen when you quit the drink. Yesterday, I was too scared to face the world. Today, it thanks me for doing just that.

Whilst drinking, I was not growing and maturing (I was being that 'late developer'). I was making up a false life to make up for the one I didn't have, and this simply made me look an idiot. As time passed and my progress slowed or failed to materialise, putting it all right with a beer was a fantastic option. After all, tomorrow would be a better day, when I would eventually:

Take responsibility.

I abdicated mine very early on, leaving my life to chance. If anything, I simply believed that everything would end up fine, without putting in any effort. I was very wrong. Things don't happen that way.

When it came to quitting alcohol, I knew I had to take responsibility. I had seen and experienced what doing nothing – merely hoping and dreaming – leads to. Nothing. This time I knew I had to put in the effort. I knew it wouldn't be immediate, but I also knew that it would be worthwhile. My family, my job, my life and happiness depended on it. This time, to develop, I was to put in the hard yards.

In doing so, I can honestly say that every aspect of my life over the last two years has become immeasurably better having finally quit. I have fantastically improved relationships with my wife and children, who have been superb in their support of me on this journey. Work has become so much more productive and enjoyable. I have also made some true and proper friends, and am able to enjoy and recall everything I get up to.

Whilst I was a heavy drinker at university, breakfast was something I generally didn't bother with as I would be nursing a hangover. When I did turn up for breakfast, and this was in halls, I would seat myself alone, a long way away from everyone else, and pray that nobody would come near me and engage in conversation of any kind. I was wholly antisocial. I would moan or grunt if anyone came near me, and only talk if there was no other option.

This was a time when I should have been building lasting friendships, engaging with other bright minds, but I chose to be alone. Not surprisingly, I wasn't really able to connect with people for the rest of the day. Who would want anything to do with that miserable git? Huge parcels of my time were being thrown away not only to drinking, but also to my being hungover, and to the effect these two had on people's desire to engage with me at all.

So, come evening time I'd find myself alone again. I would seek out a limited social life, in the bar. I simply drank and said the odd hello to other students. I never built relationships. My behaviour, looking back on it now, borne of fear and insecurity, burnt any bridges there were between me and my fellow students.

As a drinker, I was NOT a morning person. Today, even before the sun has considered peeping over the horizon, I am up and about, creating. This all takes place before my working day, my 9-to-5 job, and I will have achieved more before most people are up, more than I used to in a whole day at work.

This is what is important today, and I am not drinking. I am doing it for me, and it is having a profoundly positive impact on my life. For the first time in years I have actually made some really good friends, and I am feeling part of something. I'm just getting on with enjoying life, and it's all coming together, rather than falling apart.

Rekindle the loves you had before

Have you ever done something and simply lost track of the time? Chances are this was something you loved, were totally absorbed in, that took you to a place of peace, pleasure and enjoyment.

The way I see it, in order to remain off the drink, I need to be content with my life. Some may find contentment in calm and relaxing activities such as walking, yoga and meditation. Others enjoy rock climbing, skydiving and go-karting. Ultimately, we are all content when we are doing what we love, and what we love is already in us; we don't need to go and find anything new. In fact, quitting drinking merely opens up the time to do what we already love. This helps the quit even further, as we don't need to stress about finding something new. We can pick up where we left off.

But what if you don't know what you love? Don't worry, once you've quit, it will come bubbling up to the surface if you simply allow it to. Don't force it, it will come.

You see, when quitting drinking, one of the key things to bear in mind is that we should change as little as possible, to keep stress levels down. Concentrate your attentions on as few things as possible, and life will be manageable. Relax into your quit and it will have a much better chance of working.

When I was drinking, my attention used to be focused on stressful deadlines, on my lack of skill and ability, on my past failures and current inadequacies. I'd have all this spinning round and round in my head. It boiled down to a single issue, and that was low self-esteem. That was where my attention was focused. I dwelt on how I wasn't up to the job, that I was a failure in life and work, that I was destined for the garbage can. This, not surprisingly, was where my energy went. I put time and effort into thinking and putting myself down. To drown out this emotional distress, feeling low all the time, I drank.

Rather than trying to get out of a hole, I was hiding in it. I was concentrating on the hole, my attention was focused on the negatives, and so I expended my energy in digging myself deeper and deeper into the hole.

I needed a change. My attention was on the negative side of life and the longer it stayed there, the more negative life became. I felt I was in a Catch-22 situation. I needed to quit drinking so I could feel better about myself but equally, I needed to feel better about myself to stop drinking. It came down to a matter of priority and likelihood of success. I knew that the more I thought about something the more it became true. We see this happening all around us, all the time.

The question then came about priority and attention. It wasn't so clear whilst I was drinking, but a period of sobriety has made this something I can now describe. What it comes down to is the difference between thought and action. I was drinking to stop thinking, and thinking to stop drinking. Something had to give. In the end it comes down to difference between thoughts and actions. Actions are physical activities; you can move objects, make things, touch, feel and smell them. Thoughts are ethereal electrical signals in the brain that come and go, seemingly without rhyme or reason.

So, by taking action, actually doing something physical, we are able to change our state. Talking, discussing, mulling things over is all very well. It's all too easy to talk in the negative, consider our flaws and churn up our faults. But if we get up and do something, make something or move something we can see a result.

In the past, I could drink all day and recall nothing. In these times, my attention would drift, be nowhere in particular, and my energy would be totally lacking. I'd have no focus, no purpose, and my energy would seep away. Action was what was needed, and action is what I took.

You know people say that the more exercise you do, the livelier you feel? Well, it's true. I took action, focused my attention on my quit, and my energy flowed into it. Each day of my quit I am conscious about it, perform it actively, and feel positive about it. My sobriety is an active choice today, whereas drinking had been a passive existence. And as long as that is the case, my energy will continue to flow towards my sobriety, and not drain away towards drunkenness.

And like a lever, the further away I get from drinking, the less effort it takes to press the sober side, and the more energy I retain for other good things in life. At times, I simply have to cut out that negative self-talk I'm so good at wallowing in.

Getting in the right frame of mind to quit

When I used to play cricket, I was a batsman and I loved it. I went out to bat with the attitude that the bowler was sending the ball my way in order for me to score runs. I was confident in that belief and attitude, and I scored plenty of runs over the years. Had I gone out to bat thinking survival or I was in danger all the time, I would have been nervous, withdrawn and quickly out. It was through my approach, my attitude and a degree of confidence in my ability that I thrived. And you'll notice just one of these was my ability! In many ways, it was HOW I went about it, rather than WHAT I did.

Taking this forward, I was very much on the 'If you believe you can, you can' train. I also think what really helped was that I loved it, that I could throw myself whole-heartedly into it, and there were no distractions. Batting required focus, concentration and a clear mind to do well. It's not necessarily easy, but when it works out it's fantastic.

I wasn't aware of it at the time, but this was one of the things I picked up in life that would help me with my quit. More often than not, the things that you have to work hard for are so much more valuable than anything else. We live in a world of instant gratification, surrounded by the 'something for nothing' generation. We have had it easy for so long, that many of us simply don't know what hard work really is. I mean hard work – hours down the mines, in boiling factories, six days a week, crammed into tiny cold houses with basic food and weekly baths in a tin tub! No, I really mean it. Hard work has changed over the years, and what was an unheard of luxury just a few years ago is now considered an essential (smartphones, for instance).

So what does this really tell us, apart from my having been side-tracked into a rant about the modern world?

Playing cricket, I learned. I was coached at school and I practised in the nets in the pre-season period. I was getting ready for the upcoming games, and I wanted to be at my best. I wasn't going to be able to turn up in April or May without having done a thing since last season and expect to perform; that would have been plain daft. My belief, that 'If you believe you can, you can', was built, it didn't appear from nowhere. It can certainly start as a little thought in the back of your mind, an 'I think I can do that' moment.

We all have plenty of them. I think I could probably be able to master riding a motorbike, but I have no desire to. I could probably be able to build some nice bookcases, but I don't want to. And all we need to do when it comes to quitting drinking is grab hold of that little seed, that small thought that says, 'I think I could do that,' however small it is, and nurture it. Unlike riding a motorbike or building a bookcase, I did want to quit, and if you are here reading this, I suspect you do too. With attention, that desire will grow. Each day you nourish it with reading, studying and talking to other people in a similar situation, spending time online looking at quit sites, you will find that your initial thought grows stronger and stronger. In a sense, you are training it just like I trained in the nets before the cricket season. You will be training your 'quit-ability' and as you do, your attitude will develop from being one of wondering 'Can I do this?' to one of confidence, saying 'I can do this!'

Same words, different order, different punctuation. One enquiring, unsure, the other confident, assertive, ready for action. The thing is, our ability to quit has always been within us; it's just that it has been stifled by fear, guilt, lack of belief, social pressure and emotional turmoil. In the past, our coping mechanism had been to drink. If we all just agree that by taking a different inspirational quote and working on it – practising – becoming a master – we can progress, and that any progress we make can bring us closer to our quit, then we are all moving in the right direction. And when we are ready to go out to bat, we can be confident of success.

Simply, by putting in the pre-season training (pre-quit groundwork) you will be match fit when the season (quit) starts. Match-fit players outrun, out-play and out-manoeuvre the opposition in every aspect of the game. In our case, the opposition is alcohol, and in this particular match our ability, confidence and preparation will put us in an unassailable position. We will come out as winners. The best sportsmen also study their opposition, working out their strengths and weaknesses, so that they are best prepared for all situations and can capitalise where needed. Let us do the same with alcohol.

One final thought. All successful sportsmen keep on training, even at the top of their game, so that they stay there. We, too, must keep up the good work, maintain our learning and keep ourselves ever ready. Keeping match fit all the time, we can quash any of alcohol's attempts to sneak back into our lives with ease, but let your 'quit-fitness' drop, and you can be leaving yourselves vulnerable to relapse.

And remember: your attitude, your emotional confidence to say 'I can do this!', or 'If you believe you can, you can', is built on the solid foundations of knowledge, practice and your subsequent 'quit-fitness'.

A commitment to staying sober

As I head off to sleep at night, I now have a general idea of what I'd like to achieve the next day. Before brushing my teeth, I note down a few jobs down on a pad, alongside some things I am grateful for from the day just gone. Yesterday I was grateful for:

- Getting through a grotty day!
- Chatting with my brother.
- Warmer weather.

And my targets for today were:

- Get up early.
- Exercise.
- Write.

So, as my alarm went off this morning, I was up and out of bed. Immediately I changed into my exercise clothes and did a 20-minute workout. In no time at all I'd achieved two out of my three daily targets and now, showered and having eaten breakfast, I'm up and running with target number three, writing.

When I don't start the day with such a committed blast of activity, I feel low and lethargic, as if I'm not really a part of the world. That was what happened yesterday and it turned into a rubbish day, one that was about getting through and getting to bed early to bring it to an end. That sort of day happens rarely now, and I know how to get through them – without alcohol.

I'm finding this new early rising routine really helping with keeping my quit, you see, which is why I've brought it up. By committing to rising early I absolutely have to go to bed earlier. This means that I literally have no opportunity to drink, or even think about it, in the evening. After work, family time, bootcamp, showering and dinner, I have about an hour when I can read for a bit and start getting ready for bed. And because I know I'll be up again the next day, I don't even think about a drink.

I've always enjoyed exercise and I've always enjoyed writing, and now that I'm not drinking I can do them both more. I haven't forced a new habit or hobby on myself, they were always there; it's just that I can now enjoy them more.

Lock and key

This new way of starting the day, which I manage most but not all of the time, has been like a key to me. I have used it to lock the door on my past drinking. Today, I treasure my life and my sobriety. By having locked a door on alcohol, I would need to open it, and do so very consciously, to let it back in. I have no desire to do that.

But before I got this side of the door and locked it against alcohol, I had to get myself out of where I was, wrapped in a cycle of drink, regret, shame, fear and hiding. I was stuck in a downward spiral heading, I guess, to ultimate ruin. Of course, I never thought that would happen to me; it was a problem for other people, and I wasn't like them. They drank differently from me. I know I'm fortunate today. I did manage to get out, to free myself from self-destruction. I found the right key.

The key as a guide

The purpose of a key is twofold. A key will open, and it will close. Unlock, and lock. There's another purpose as well. A key also helps us break a code. Diagrams will have a key that tells us what certain symbols mean. Without the key, we can't decipher the symbols or work out the instructions; we don't understand what is in front of us. The key helps us read the manual. They are like shortcuts, providing a picture rather than a thousand words. They are representations, and we like pictures; our minds work well with them.

We all have our own ways of working, getting through life and, like anything else, functioning best. As such, we all have our own instruction manuals, and unless we understand our own instruction manual we won't necessarily work to the best of our abilities. We may even find that we malfunction, and this could manifest itself in all sorts of ways, one of which could be drinking alcoholically or at least to excess. However, if we fully understand that manual, by having the right key, then this should not happen, or it can be put right if it goes wrong.

Like a car, we can prevent ourselves from breaking down, but only if we maintain ourselves as per the manual.

The right key

As well as instruction manuals, cars also have keys. Without a key, a car will not start. Further, a Vauxhall key will not start a Ford. Your Mondeo key will not start my Mondeo. There will only be one key that starts one specific car. As a drinker, you are as individual as your car, and there's only one key to open you, to start you up as a non-drinker. To break the drinking cycle, you need to find that key, or even make it yourself.

But what, you might ask, is that key made of? What does it look like? For each of you, I don't know, but I know what mine looks like and how I made it:

Mine is made of a bit of AA, some Allen Carr, plenty of Annie Grace, many hangovers, some vomit and plenty of bed sweats. Interspersed with these there are some memorable nights out, good times and laughs. There's a sprinkling of blood and bruising from falling over, the occasional comment I should never have made, and a much lower balance in my savings account that there would otherwise have been. Add to that lots of reading and research, failed attempts and hollow promises, and you'll see the key is a complicated little thing, and intensely personal. Give me *your* key and I'd drink again, as you would if you tried mine.

You will have to forge your own key, and it may take some time. Once you have it, you can open the door on sobriety, lock it closed on alcohol, read the instructions, and start a new life. Your key will do all this for you. I can't give it to you on a plate, but it will come to you if you look, and work, hard enough for it.

But it's not all plain sailing. So often my addiction had me close the manual, throw away the key and behave in the most peculiar ways.

286

Get out of the kitchen

If you can't stand the heat, get out of the kitchen.

Well, if it were only that easy. As an alcoholic drinker, the idea that we can just turn around, take ourselves out of the situation and be free is extremely attractive. I recall this being called a 'geographical' from my days in AA. In this situation, the alcoholic, you or me, has a belief that moving away from an area – our hometown, for example, where we know the pubs and drinkers and constantly find ourselves drawn into them – will remove these temptations and give us a fresh start. In a new town nobody knows us, so won't be aware of our drinking past. We believe we won't be tempted to call on a friend, or go into an unknown pub. We believe that simply moving to a different part of the country will solve the problem. Moving away, we can leave all our troubles behind. And it's so common it has gained the name of a 'geographical'.

The thing is there's nothing wrong with where you are, your kitchen. The problem, if we are to call it that, is in you. When you move, you simply take the problem with you. Within days, hours or even minutes of finding yourself in a new town, your problem will pop up and suggest finding the nearest pub, off-licence, beer festival, whatever. And there's a bonus of being in a new town; nobody knows you so you don't have to worry about where you buy your booze. Nobody will notice. In some ways, you have just made the situation worse.

As the issue is in you, then going somewhere else, getting out of the kitchen but taking it with you, may

287

actually be more like jumping out of the frying-pan and into the fire.

So, if moving isn't the best option and leaving your peers behind isn't going to help, then we stay where we are. Better the devil you know? Probably, but we can also look at ourselves as being in an abusive relationship that we want to get out of. Consider that. Individuals co-exist in abusive relationships for considerable lengths of time. I don't pretend to know much about these, but from what I can gather these relationships hold together for one of two reasons: first, one partner forces the other to stay through the use of threats, and second, there is some mutual need that keeps people together when to the outside world it appears to make no sense to.

Ditto alcohol. It's an abusive partner, and its highly addictive nature means that it has an incredibly strong and illogical hold over us. It may be killing us, but we need it. Leaving it behind and moving away, getting out of the kitchen, becomes inconceivable. In time, it becomes our only friend, our one reliable partner. Its reliability is exactly what makes it so powerful and so dangerous. It is always there for us when we need it, and it makes sure we always need it. It is a friend we could well do without.

Living with an abusive partner can never be a pleasant experience, but we also know breaking away from such a relationship is incredibly hard. Many of us will never experience it, but we see and hear of the horrors and tragedies that befall the lives of others. Many people need huge amounts of support for this, and so it is with alcohol. Alcohol may be the abusive partner, but it's also a balm for many. With its two-faced nature, it really is a smiling assassin, killing you slowly.

288

If it helps you, seek help from others. Go to AA, find a counsellor, speak to your family and friends (real friends, not your drinking buddies). Use the support network around you. You know full well that you would help a friend in need, so remember everyone else will do the same for you as well. It may be hard to see, but it's true; you have an invisible network, so use it. Don't do a 'geographical'. All the help you need is exactly where you are now.

Some of that help may be useful, some may not be. I found that counselling didn't work for me, but I didn't know that before I started. It could be just the thing for you, so try everything. You will find what you need, what ticks your boxes, and when you do, you'll know.

Maybe you need a 'safe house', as it were. This could be rehab for a while, or just finding somewhere in your own home where you can be at peace. Need your safe house be of bricks and mortar? Maybe not. Perhaps you could seek it in your own mind through meditation, walks in nature, literature even. Getting out of the kitchen, doing a 'geographical', it's a state of mind, not a physical thing. Today, I find walking and reading incredibly uplifting. They are totally accessible to everyone, involve very little effort and bring massive calm, and thus results.

Rather than moving away and taking our problems with us, we recognise them for what they are and where they are. Maybe think of it like turning down the gas, rather than leaving the kitchen. That way you are taking control, not fleeing. When quitting, keeping it as simple as possible is key. Introducing new stresses such as moving away may hinder, not help, your quest.

Don't run, don't hide, but do look around, open your eyes. You will find what you need, just where you are, just when you need it. My neighbour Stuart came up and sat with me one day in September 2019, when I was lost and frightened in a pub garden. I was just where I needed to be. He saved my life. With a closed mind and a 'geographical' I would not have been there, and I might have lost everything by now. Instead, I have to admit, my life has never been richer. Moreover, that's because I didn't get out of the kitchen.

The final piece of support that I needed to achieve my quit appeared to me that afternoon, for just an hour or so, and then he was gone. Because I had my eyes open, I saw it for what it was, and because of the work I had done before, the reading and preparation (failed attempts, false promises and so on), I was ready to embrace it when it came. This work had allowed me to take control of the kitchen, so that when it really did get too hot on that September day I knew I must, could and would happily turn off the gas.

It was only when all the pieces came together that I was able to quit. Seeing that happen was what made the difference. I certainly hadn't made plans to quit that day, but when it came to it, it was the right day to and I was ready. Most importantly, I was THERE.

It was then that I ended the relationship and broke up with alcohol. This time, there was to be no trial separation.

Breaking up

'Me and alcohol? Yeah, we've been together for 15 years now, that's right. We actually moved in together after just six months; it was all a bit of a whirlwind really. For me, it was like love at first sight (sip!). Infatuation? Probably a good word to describe it, yes.

'We've had our ups and downs over the years, for sure. We even had a trial separation a year or so ago, but our love proved too strong. We only lasted a few weeks apart and were straight back together.

'Would I call it love? It was at the start, yes. But now, I'm not so sure. We kinda just go together, don't we? I mean, we're totally suited, aren't we? Can you imagine us being alone? No, we come together, like a package holiday!'

OK, farfetched I know; but there's more than an ounce of truth in there, don't you agree? Do you recognise anything with how you and alcohol get along? As a drinker, I certainly felt that the two of us were inseparable. The relationship started well, then deteriorated, and over time became unbearable, but still we stuck together.

We had been like friends, lovers, companions, all rolled into one. We had been together for years, so alcohol became such a part of my life that it was a defining characteristic. I was a heavy drinker and, although few people would say anything, it was what first came to mind for many. For some, it was a total shock when I told them! Oh, I could function all right, but I was never going to shine. Not everybody does, so that didn't look unusual. I thought I could get away with it, and I did for a long time.

Then there came a point when I could carry on no longer. I knew I had to stop. All would be lost if I didn't, and I was scared – of failing and of succeeding. The fear of failure saw me declining to a sad and lonely death. The fear of success saw me not understanding how to function without my friend by my side, my crutch, my constant companion, my alcohol. How would I cope alone? Would I be on the bounce and looking for something else?

But I knew we had to break up; this relationship was not a happy one. Alcohol had its claws in me and wasn't willing to let go. In every way it had me trapped. Emotionally, physically and socially, I needed alcohol. I also needed nothing to do with it. I couldn't talk things through with it. I couldn't reason with it. I couldn't ask it to start behaving more reasonably towards me. I couldn't ask it to give me a bit of space, to try some other form of entertainment together, maybe. Alcohol is a one-dimensional partner and it will not change its ways. It simply can't.

I'd tried to kick alcohol out before, with varying degrees of success. Well, when I say varying degrees of success that's not true. When it comes to quitting, there's either success or there isn't. A varying degree would mean I had quit partly, say a third or a quarter, or for a week, a month, whatever. But they aren't quits. Quit means a permanent stop. Anything else might be called a break or cutting down. When it comes to quitting, these are not successes. Let's not dress them up, they are failures.

You don't have a partial divorce, do you?

So, it has to be with alcohol. And you don't need to feel sympathy or emotion towards it. It is not a person. It doesn't care, think or feel. It is an addictive drug, nothing more, nothing less. Don't cut down or take a break. Getting back together only fans the flames of that toxic relationship, making it ever more deadly.

There is only one way to quit, and that is to break up permanently. Ending relationships is hard, you may feel lonely for a while, lost even. But believe me, it will be over sooner than you imagine it could be. Once you have given alcohol its marching orders, and you don't have to be tactful or caring about this breakup, you must be brutal about not letting it sneak back in. It will try and try and try. Day by day, however, its efforts will become weaker until they're so feeble you'll barely notice them. Be ruthless and crush it. You, an entire, strong and thinking being, a member of the most advanced species on earth, can beat a lifeless liquid. There should be no competition.

And once broken up, unlike you do with other human relationships, don't feel any guilt, sadness, anger towards the other party. You should try to feel nothing for it. It feels nothing for you.

You may have shared some amazing times together, had some great fun. There will also be some tragic scenes you'd rather forget, or never remembered in the first place. All sorts. Don't dwell on them, move on.

You will soon find yourself in a new relationship, one with life itself. One with the energy you'll have, with the clarity of mind, of experience. You will dance in the delight of your senses:

- You'll see better.
- You'll hear more clearly.
- You'll taste food like never before.
- You'll experience scents all over again.

- You'll even have a better sense of touch.

You'll be in love with yourself again. And not long into your quit, you may even ask yourself, 'How would alcohol make this better?' The clear answer will be, 'It wouldn't.'

Taking alcohol away from your life will give you so much more. Breaking up may seem hard, but it's the best thing you could ever do for yourself. Just remember, this relationship is a one-way street, heading to hell. Break up now.

Instant gratification vs long-term goals

Maybe this is just me, but does it seem that everyone wants something for nothing now? Do people expect immediate results? Has everyone run out of patience? I think so. One click and it's there. Rapid this, immediate that, next-day delivery (even quicker), instant noodles, Deliveroo: effort no longer seems to play much of a part in our lives.

Here in 2021, we want even more, every day. We didn't have social media in 1989, and now it dominates our lives, putting many of us, especially the younger generations under huge pressure. It's relentless and omnipresent, disturbing or lives like they have never been disturbed before. And yes, on the whole, social media posts glorify alcohol.

That's it, really.

Get pissed quick!

Oh, and it's all very funny. You see, I often cook with wine, sometimes I even put it in the food! Haha! Come on, surely it's Wine O'clock by now? Wherever we look, it's booze, drinking and hilarity all rolled into one. And it's there for the taking, no effort involved. Fancy a pizza? Yeah, deliver some beers with that, please. There are even these bloody robotic fridges cruising my hometown now, delivering food and drink. Come on, wake up, will you!?

But quitting? Doing that requires something many of us have had little practice at in this world, working hard for something. And I mean working hard, harder than you've ever worked before. You will be facing seemingly insurmountable problems, working out solutions to overcome them, over and over again. You'll be on your own much of the time, and you'll have little more than what seems like a tattered old guidebook to help you through. You'll need to find your own way, through dedicated graft, kept up over time. You'll have plenty of failures and find numerous dead ends. This is what the greats of the world have done over the centuries – refined their craft by constant attention and practice.

You can't order a takeaway quit.

Consider the single mindedness of Steve Jobs, Mother Theresa, and Gandhi. These are some of the greatest humans ever. You may not be one of these, but to achieve greatness in your quit you can learn from them. Being brilliant is not a part-time occupation, nor is it for a few days. It's constant and it requires dedication. And rather than being one big, crowd-pleasing firework, your quit will be the daily accumulation of constant, tiny wins. These will go by unnoticed until, when the time comes and you quit, people will look up and wonder how you did it overnight.

You did not and you'll know it. This journey is nothing like the instant gratification of the needy. And because of that, your quit will last. You will be at peace with a decision you have made, because it will be one that is balanced, considered and thoughtful. It is not an instant, here today/gone tomorrow flash of celebrity. It is the new, forever you, and I recommend you work on it, come what may. For the prize at the end is life itself.

Ever-increasing volumes

One of the strangest things about quitting, or rather our multiple attempts at quitting, is how our drinking changes over time. What I mean is that each time we have a period of not drinking we tend to end up drinking more when we go back to it that we did when we started a sober period. It's almost as if we are trying to catch up for lost time, but perhaps it's actually more sinister than that.

This is a phenomenon known by most, if not all, drinkers. It wouldn't surprise me at all if it was also used by many to allow them to keep on drinking. After all, if stopping for a period of time means you'll end up drinking even more later on, then surely it's going to be more harmful quitting than carrying on? If that's the case, I'll not stop, we could say.

But why would it be that when we stop and restart, we end up drinking more than we did before we took a break from it? Surely a good cleanse, and being without for a while (thus decreasing our tolerance to it) would mean we'd want to drink less, not more. And yes, that's true, we would *want* to drink less.

But we'd *need* to drink more, and we all know that there's a world of difference between what we want and what we need.

The issue here is that drinking is a progressive habit and, on the whole, the amount we tend to drink will always increase over time. As we go through life we tend not to reduce our alcohol intake. As children we consume none. We experiment as teenagers, drink socially at weekends as we move through our 20s and 30s, then settle at home, every night, with a bottle of wine in our 40s and 50s.

Perhaps we drink at lunchtime as we retire, and start earlier in the day as we age. Over time we drink more, and more often.

This progression will always be there, and oddly enough it does not stop its march when we go through a sober period. For those of us with a drink problem this is merely more pronounced, but it happens to everyone. The amount we drink goes up over time. When we take a break, that increase still takes place in the background, so when we start again we re-join the drinking line higher up the graph, right away. The trajectory of our drinking has continued to rise ahead of us, and when we get back on it's higher than when we got off. The longer we are sober, the bigger the increase that has been going on unseen.

Yes, it's a progressive problem and the only way to avoid it is to remain quit. If you turn your back on alcohol completely, this progression can carry on (and will anyway) without your having to worry about it. As you'll never get back on the booze, it's not relevant. Stop for short or long periods though and you'll re-join your drinking trajectory at a much higher level, and you'll wonder why you bothered. Alcohol is a tricky little beast like that, trying to convince us that it's better to carry on drinking than it is to stop.

So, stopping and starting will actually be counterproductive, as we'll start to believe that carrying on is a better option. IT IS NOT. It never will be. We all tend to consume more and more rather than less and less as we go through life. Understanding this is critical, and we can see it all around us.

When you make the decision to quit, remember that the only way to avoid this problem of increasing consumption after a quit is to become a non-drinker, and to remain one. Knowing what that means, and why, is also a powerful tool in ensuring you stay away from booze. Believe me, after a substantial amount of time without a drink I really don't want to find out where I'd re-join my drinking curve! And that's incentive enough to keep away from it!

Further, the fewer things you need to think about when you quit, the better. Do your best to keep things simple.

Reconciliation, win-win

Often, our behaviour goes against our beliefs. We know we should not drink and yet we do. We should not smoke, yet we light a cigarette. Gambling is a bad idea, yet we continue to feed the one-armed bandit with more coins. I'm sure you can think of many, many more examples.

In our minds, we are like two warring nations or, worse still, one nation suffering the ravages of a civil war. We are behaving like two intransigent businessmen trying to strike a deal. With neither side willing to step down, we have stalemate. If we stay here, nothing will get resolved. The situation on the ground will deteriorate, and we will be unable to move forwards. Somehow or other we need to break this stalemate and come out the other side. We need to go through a period of negotiation and reconciliation.

In the world of politics and business, there are people who specialise in these activities, but we don't have access to them. But we do know what they are aiming for and some of the potential outcomes. We want to stop drinking, to quit, and not go back to it again. For that, we need to be settled, or reconciled, in our quit.

Our ancient brain says we should drink, and modern brain says NO. There's a civil war going on in there. Is it any wonder we turn to drink to try and get away from that turmoil? I know I did. I'm sure you do, too. Ultimately, drinking our way through this war isn't going to bring about peace. We may have tried for years and the results show for themselves. The war rages on.

Somehow we need to get to a point where we can call a ceasefire and sign a peace treaty. For this, we can turn our attention to the process of negotiation, and look at the possible outcomes.

Today, drinking and wishing we were not, we are in a lose-lose position. Our modern brain knows that drinking is bad for us, but we drink. It isn't impressed. Our ancient brain insists we drink, but is constantly berated for this. It, also, isn't impressed. Neither side is happy, each feels hard done by, and each feels undermined. It feels like it has lost. Lose-lose.

Two other positions are as follows:

- Win-lose
- Lose-win

In win-lose, let's say the modern brain emerges victorious and we manage to quit. We have managed to exert authority over the troublesome ancient brain, put it in its place and silenced it. Our modern brain has 'won'; we have quit and we should be delighted. But we're not. Inside of us we still have that ancient brain, and it's like a prisoner, a POW in our analogy. Outside, it has allies who will fight its corner when it can't do so for itself. Whilst we are exerting energy to maintain our authority over it, that authority is being challenged. In this situation, the ancient brain has 'lost', but it continues to fight from within and from outside. By making it a loser, we have not changed it in any way at all, we have merely angered it. Our minds remain out of balance, and our angered ancient brain will continue to make life uncomfortable for us. Carry on like this, and we'll crumble one day. We will drink again. We can't keep this up forever.

Next up, we hit the lose-win scenario. Not where we want to be at all, this is abject surrender where we allow our ancient brain to run roughshod over our logic and our need to quit. This is where we throw our hands in the air and say, 'I simply can't do it, I'm doomed. It's all too much for me.' Our modern brain has lost. It will be deeply saddened, and will remind us of this each and every day. It may cause us to beat ourselves up time and time again. For as long as we allow it to be bullied by our ancient brain, it will remind us that we chose this path. Our ancient brain may have won, but all it has won is a barren land, stripped bare by the ravages of the war we have been waging. It is a hollow victory.

But then there's the final position, the one where everyone is happy. We call this win-win. This is a place of harmony, peace, balance and quiet. The war is over, our minds exist together, respect one another and no longer fight, for there is no need to. Our ancient brain has come to a point where its drive to help us survive is satisfied, it understands we are healthier, wealthier and wiser without the booze. It now drives us to good food, company, exercise and genuine relaxation. Our modern brain can now relax, enjoy the advances of the modern world, use its huge potential of logic and creative thinking for good, to bring progress into our lives. Neither has the upper hand, neither is subjugated. In this place, we don't even consider a drink, let alone have an internal discussion about it.

On our journey to a quit, let's head for a win-win position. Keep this simple concept in mind. How you design your quit is up to you, for a quit is as individual as you are. All quits, to stand the test of time and last, need to conclude in a place of balance, and a win-win place is about as good as it gets.

Overthinking things

When you realise it's the right time for you to quit, don't fanny about – decide and GO FOR IT – leave no space for doubt – there should be none anyway, but make sure you leave no room for it.

I spend so much time thinking about things that never get done. I am forever spinning up projects in my mind, imagining how great they'll be, building them up into great business or personal ventures that give me freedom and happiness, wealth and cars. None has come to anything.

Oh, I have a small personal training venture, but that's not really going to set the world on fire or make me famous! But I do love it and want to keep it the way it is; it works for me. And I'm writing this, whilst running my full-time job and a sideline business. And still I fill the spare hours with dreams.

As a drinker I was no different. I would sit there for hours on end imagining how good life could be if I stopped. I went everywhere, did everything, inside my head. And I got nowhere, physically, emotionally or spiritually.

The only way you can stop is by taking action. Spinning ideas round and round inside your head may feel productive, even fun and exciting, but only by actually doing something will anything change.

You may have a thousand quit ideas going around in your head. If they stay there you will continue to drink. Grab hold of one, act on it, and you will progress so much more quickly to your final, successful, quit.

And when you have found that quit, love and nurture it.

Own and love your quit

One night, I was chatting to an old friend on the phone for a good couple of hours. He'd been a drinking buddy for years and is still astounded that I managed to quit, totally and immediately, all that time ago. As we were speaking, he was wishing I could bottle up my secret and cure the world. Yes, he'd had a drink by then. In fact he'd answered the phone with an apology for having had a couple of beers. It was Saturday night – of course he had!

Put simply, he was astounded that I was just so quiet about my quit and I merely said,

'Yeah, I just knew the time had come and so I stopped.'

'Yes,' he said, 'but that's not it, is it, Jonesy?'

Actually, it is.

The drinking was done with. The sickness and tiredness was done with. My years of research into the effects of drinking were done with. My reading about quitting had become a key aspect of my life. I had matured. And, above all else, I understood that alcohol no longer served a purpose in my life. It hadn't for some time, but now I understood, accepted and acted upon that.

Simply put, all the drinks I had had, all the books I had read, all the courses and therapies I had attended, added up to the point where I could say to Paul, 'Yes, it is that simple.'

The act of quitting was simple, is simple.

Arrival at a destination is as simple as stepping off a train. In the case of quitting a life of alcohol, that train is more of a rollercoaster, but even they come to a smooth stop to let the revellers off.

I am quiet about my quit. When people ask me how I did it I tell them it was an immediate and sudden stop. It was, except that it started ten years before and took in about every possible type of attempt on the way, bar rehab. The outside world sees the fruits of my labour. It does not see or hear the backstory. Success, great success, is not built on an immediate flash of inspiration one day, and completion of building the empire the next. It's built on hard work and dedication. It's built on determination to get somewhere, dogged determination.

People love rags to riches stories. They give us all hope. We want to hear how a low-born fellow came to create the biggest company in the world; such fascinating lives they lead. These extraordinary people all have something in common, though. That common factor is simple drive, determination and hard work. Hard work.

Maybe I'm flippant when I say, 'Yes, it's that simple,' when it comes to quitting, but you don't need a certain intellect, a certain background, certain networks and contacts. It comes down to hard work and graft. If you don't expose yourself to and involve yourself in finding out what quitting is all about, and if you don't try its possible tools and techniques and master some, then you'll not arrive at sobriety. If you do, and you want it with the determination capable of delivering world-class results, then you will. To be a world-class success story takes just one thing. Work. Work guarantees results.

My quit is incredibly important to me. Some people admire me for it, look at me and say, 'How did he do that?' The rest of the world couldn't give a hoot. If people want to know about it, I'll tell them, even give them some of the detail.

Otherwise I just say, 'That's right, I stopped a few years ago and, yeah, I love it.'

Quitting may take a few attempts – so what?

Yeah, so what!

In so many walks of life we hear of people overcoming adversity, defying the odds. And very often they emerge the stronger for it. You can bet your bottom dollar that they had more than just the one attempt at breaking free, overcoming their difficulties, proving their strength and resilience. They will have faced challenges and setbacks along the way. But they all kept coming back, and triumphed in the end.

In Japan, there's an ancient saying that encapsulates this perfectly:

'Fall seven times, rise eight.'

When we give anything a go, it is not the falling down that matters, it is the getting up and giving it another go until you succeed that does. Watch a toddler learning to walk. He is not deterred when he falls, he'll often giggle at this point, landing back down on his bum. He'll smile his way through grabbing the sofa to hold himself steady, then stepping into the unknown of the open carpet, faltering and collapsing. He'll relish the challenge, and never be put off by what we'd term as failure – falling. Pretty soon, he'll be walking and having even more fun exploring the world that has opened up to him at this new height, one metre above the carpet!

Maybe you have tried to quit drinking before. Did you quit? I mean, if you did, you wouldn't be drinking now, you wouldn't be reading this book about quitting, unless it

307

simply interests you, in which case I'm flattered. So now I presume you are back, thinking about giving it another go. There's something important here and it's that, in spite of the adversity you have faced, the fact that you have tried to quit and failed (I guess), you are back and giving it another go. In the words of author Don MacNaughton:

'Adversity is often for many people a fact of life, but rather than letting difficulties keep them down, people with high resilience find a way to get back up.'

What it doesn't mean is that you are immune to setbacks. Stuff happens, even to those with high resilience. The thing is that they will accept this, adapt the way they act and overcome the difficulty.

The good news here is that you can also learn resilience, how to make yourself better at coming back. And on one of those comebacks, you'll find your quit. McNaughton suggests the following to help build your resilience, your comeback-ability, but I've put them in my own words:

- Focus on your current abilities (build your self-confidence through them).
- Set small and realistic goals (walk before you can run).
- Try to get your inner voice to talk positively about you (you can try the 'fake it 'til you make it' routine – it works!).
- Pause before you react.

Baby steps, that's what we need. That's all the toddler needed and he got to walk. He'd never walked before. You

308

have the advantage over him of having lived sober before –
you, unlike him, know what's ahead.

And remember:

If at first you don't succeed, try, try again.

It really doesn't matter how many times you fall before
you get up that very last time because, once you get there,
you'll soon forget all the failed attempts and remember just
the one successful one. You'll remember only the good,
none of the bad, and that will add further strength to your
already successful quit.

Go in relaxed

So what if you have umpteen Day 1s? Does it really matter that you need to keep trying again, and that you don't manage to quit first time? I don't think so. The very fact that you keep coming back to Day 1 shows you have resilience and determination. Yes, it can be frustrating having to start all over again, but behind every new Day 1 is a small (or larger) success, a period when you weren't drinking, and that can never be taken away. Look at this in a positive way: however long that quit lasted, it lasted longer that if you hadn't done it. Your body, at the very least, will have appreciated a break from the constant barrage of booze!

And so what if you have a drink as you try to master your quit? None of us is perfect, and pretty much nobody gets anything right first time. Have a look around you. Did all this modern world appear in one go, out of nowhere? Of course not; it appeared after years, decades, of development, trials and experimentation. You are, in fact, in good company. Some of the best changes in history have come from long periods of hard work. Look at medicine, for instance. Years of research and development goes into each and every new drug on the market; they don't appear fully formed and complete. And they are developed by people who do this all the time. You are new to this, and having a few false starts is normal. I fell off my bike learning to ride it, but I can ride it now. I'm sure you, too, can ride a bike, where once you couldn't. Quitting drinking is the same – learning a new skill – so don't get fazed by it.

Remember that you must be selfish in your quit; it is yours and yours alone. Try to ensure you don't get distracted by what others might think of you or what you think of them. In this, they are irrelevant. You are totally in charge, and that allows you to approach your quit your way, and you will not be deflected by others. For a while, honestly, don't worry about anyone else but yourself and you will, I guarantee, be a lot more relaxed about the whole process, which is an enormous benefit you give yourself.

When you quit, a few things will happen to your body and mind. Go with the flow, relax and enjoy the process. Feel the quit grow, feel the alcohol drift away. As each moment passes, early on in your quit, you will FEEL different, your mind will THINK differently. You will have new experiences, and you should savour them, as they are signs that your quit is taking hold, that alcohol is being banished.

If you get tired when you quit, sleep! (You will want to.)

Want sugary stuff? Have it. The booze had loads in it, so your body will miss it. Don't annoy your body, let it have sugar if it wants it. I particularly love white chocolate, so I have it.

And if you want to treat yourself to something, do it!

Be impulsive; it's fun!

Read, dance, sing, celebrate, life gets better every day. Decide that's how your quit will be – FUN – and it will be.

For me, that meant going to more gigs (I now have the money to do this, and I can remember them all!) and going out for more runs. I'm just back from a Sunday morning 10-miler and feel full of energy. As well as that, I now do far more bootcamps, and love being out walking in nature with my wife. Just these last few days the green buds of spring are starting to come through in the hedges, the snowdrops are coming out and winter aconites are blooming. I'm noticing these things now, taking pleasure in what's around me. Taking things slowly, with a laid-back attitude. I'm able to see the beauty in things, to appreciate the world I live in far more than before. And why? Because I am now actively living in it, not just passing through in some kind of coma.

I'm also reading far more than I used to, and at work, I'm more productive and effective. My stress levels have plummeted, and I just get on with it now. I don't have anything to prove and as a result I don't fret. I'm getting done in a day what used to take me a week, and every day still has the same 24 hours as before.

Without booze to stress me out, life is pretty damn good! You should try it yourself – you might like it!

What's so great about quitting?

I trust we all agree that drinking as we do, alcoholically or at least to excess, is doing us more harm than good? And we all agree that we should stop altogether, so that we don't slide back down the inevitable slippery slope to excess drinking once again? Further, we also understand that for us, cutting down doesn't work? Great. So that means our lives are going to change quite substantially from now on in, and we are going to face all sorts of situations we didn't before. So, that being the case, what is so great about being sober all the time? What makes it such a special place that we would want to live there, and never drink again, ever?

Without effort, I can reel off SIX massive advantages that you will encounter each and every day for the rest of your lives. These are my six 'mores', and they are as follows. You will have:

1. More friends.
2. More time.
3. More money.
4. More choices.
5. More freedom.
6. More energy.

1.   More friends.

Yes, certainly. In our drinking days we had a few good mates and drinking buddies, or we may have been isolated (even when we were with them). Quit drinking and a few of those friends actually no longer appeal, as it was only really getting drunk with each other that kept you together. You may find that some encourage you to keep drinking. These people are against you, they are not your friends. Soon enough, you'll meet up with new people and, as I have found to be absolutely the case, you'll be drawn towards a more attractive and more sober crowd, with greater balance in their lives, but no less fun. In the last year, even in lockdown (it's early February 2021 in the UK now), I have laughed more and made deeper and more lasting friendships than at any other time in my life. Why? Because I am genuinely interested in these people, and being sober and clear headed, can engage with them with deeper respect. As your sobriety matures and your self-confidence grows, you will naturally find friendships easier to make, and to keep.

2. More time.

Every day consists of 24 hours and, when drinking, we all kiss goodbye to a few of them. We waste them drunk, we waste them hungover and we waste them planning drinking. Even at a very conservative level, let's say we fritter away two hours a day, which isn't unreasonable. Over a year that equates to over 700 hours, or 30 days, that's a MONTH of life. That, my friends, is a scary amount of time, and if you quit drinking that's the extra time that you'll get back. Without a doubt, quitting drinking gives us all more time to do great things with our lives. And that leads us onto my next 'more'.

3. More money.

Of course, with more time, you might need more money, and you are going to get it. I used to buy, on average, two bottles of wine a day. I'd have beer as well, and gin, and drink more at the weekend and on holiday, but let's stick to two bottles average. At £5 each bottle, that's £3,650 every year (just over £5,000 pre-tax). Imagine your boss giving you a FIVE GRAND pay rise! However much you earn, that's a whopping sum, and it's yours for the taking, to do what you want with, and it starts rolling in at the rate of £10 a day, from the morning you wake up and have stopped drinking. That flow of tenners will keep going forever if you allow it to. When you quit, the supply is unlimited, so long as you stay quit. Nice bonus! Nobody can argue with that. And now that you have more money, and more time, you'll naturally have...

4.   More choices.

This one is even better now as well. Not only do you have more time to do stuff, and more money to do it with, but you'll also be sober and will enjoy everything that much more. You'll be fully there, involved in what you are doing and, this time round, you'll remember it all. No more blackouts! Funnily enough, you'll also end up making better choices. Where, previously, what you did revolved around drinking (yes, it did), that will no longer be the case. The list of possibilities that opens up will now include everything. All restrictions are lifted. Life becomes richer.

Who wouldn't want an extra month a year, with money to spend doing fun new things with your friends? It does sound attractive, doesn't it? And it is yours for the taking. Not drinking gives you just that, but it also gives you...

5.   More freedom.

Before quitting, your life revolved around booze. Kick that into touch and you are no longer a slave to it. You can

315

go anywhere, anytime, with anyone. Drinking restricted you, imprisoned you, enslaved you. Put down the drink and that life ends. You are immediately and permanently free. You have seen how it can be done, picking your own way through the choices and creating your own quit. It's now your choice and, if I were you, I'd choose freedom.

6. More energy.

With your newfound freedom, extra time, new friends, cash in hand, and the world at your feet to do what you please, you'll be delighted that quitting will give you tons more energy. Drinking and lethargy go hand in hand. Get sober and you'll be brighter, livelier and more energetic than you can imagine. You'll sleep far better, rise brighter and keep going longer and this level of extra energy means you will enjoy the five 'mores' to the max.

This is what I have found from quitting, and I believe you will, too. These are not big, bold, out-of-this-world promises, they are all very simple and down to earth. They are also true, and they are absolutely there for you if you work for them. Perhaps best of all, they start coming true the very second you put down the drink, and you can see and feel them happening. As the alcohol leaves your body, you'll feel physically better within hours, and the money will start accumulating right away. Those are the best proofs you can have, and you don't need anything special to make them come true. You just need to put into practice what you have learned in here and from your wider research, and quit.

With these tools, you can and you will. I'm sure of it.

Acknowledgements

Writing my first book, I had no idea that so many people would help me along the way. There are of course too many to mention everyone, and if I've had a drink or two with you in the past, you are, of course, one of them! There are those of you I simply won't recall for obvious reasons, and for that I apologise.

On a more down to earth note, I'd like to thank all those at 3P Publishing. For the help and encouragement of Andy Gibney, Caroline Snelling and Lauren Butler in bringing it all to life, to Julia Thorley, my editor, for her straight-talking critiques, and to James Mossop for his fantastic artwork and cover design.

I'd especially like to thank Paul Pateman, Steve Green, and Dylan Jones, for their helpful feedback on the early drafts, without which this book would never have developed as it has done. To Mark Kennedy, Jan Morter, Richard Chatley, Paul Brooksbank and Sophy Humphreys for your wonderful support. Roger Taylor has been a star for my website, as well as a great and sober friend throughout. To all at Be Military Fit Northampton, Northampton Road Runners and Queens Park Fitness, you have all helped in ways you can only imagine.

A special mention must go to Stuart Cal, who found me alone and lost in the pub, and whose appearance and kind words that day were the catalyst to stop me drinking, from that point onwards. You saved my life!

And most importantly, thank you to my wonderful wife, Helen, for standing by me through thick and thin.

I love you x

Further Reading

Grace, A. 2020. This Naked Mind. Glasgow, HQ Publishing.

Gray, C. 2017. The Unexpected Joy of Being Sober. New Jersey, Aster.

Beck, C. 2017. Alcohol Lied to Me. Independently published.

Carr, A. 2009. Easy Way to Control Alcohol. London, Arcturus.

Porter, W. 2015. Alcohol Explained. California, CreateSpace.

Vale, J. 2011. Kick the Drink. . .Easily! Carmarthen, Crown House Publishing.

AA. 2002. The Story of How Many Thousands of Men and Women Have Recovered from Alcoholism. Minnesota, Hazelden Publishing.

Sharma, R. 2018. The 5AM Club. New York.

Jeffers, S. 2019. Feel the Fear and Do It Anyway. California, Hay House Inc Publishing.

McGonigal, K. 2013. The Willpower Instinct. New York, Avery Publishing Group.

Duhigg, C. 2013. The Power of Habit. Manhattan, Random House Publishing.